Faith

Developing an Adult Spirituality

Student Exercise Book

Carla E. Fritsch

William J. Raddell Jr.

Edward G. Scheid

Series Title	*Discipleship in the Catholic Tradition*
The Authors	Carla E. Fritsch, who earned her M.A. at John Carroll University, Cleveland, Ohio, is a religion teacher and theology department chairperson. She has served as coauthor and editor of various curriculum units in The Center for Learning's Faith and Novel/Drama series.
	William J. Raddell Jr., who earned his Masters in Pastoral Studies at Loyola University of Chicago, is a religion teacher and theology department chairperson and has served as a religious education consultant for The Center for Learning. He is also the coauthor and editor of various books in the Discipleship in the Catholic Tradition series.
	Edward G. Scheid, who earned his M.Ed. in religious education from Boston College and his Ph.D. in theology from Duquesne University, is a principal and former religion teacher. He has written for the Center for Learning's Catholic Teaching series and Discipleship in the Catholic Tradition series.
The Publishing Team	Rose Schaffer, HM, M.A., President/Chief Executive Officer Bernadette Vetter, HM, M.A., Vice President Mary Jane Simmons, HM, M.A., Vice President, Editorial Linda Valasik, HM, M.M., Coordinator, Religion Division Diana Culbertson, OP, Ph.D., Editor Tammy Sanderell, B.A., Editor
Art Direction	Krina K. Walsh, B.S.I.D.
Nihil Obstat	The Reverend John F. Loya, M.A., M.Div. Censor Deputatus
Imprimatur	The Most Reverend Anthony M. Pilla, D.D., M.A. Bishop of Cleveland

Given at Cleveland, Ohio, on 2 April 2004.

The *Nihil Obstat* and *Imprimatur* are official declarations that a book or pamphlet is free of doctrinal or moral error. No implication is contained therein that those who have granted the *Nihil Obstat* and *Imprimatur* agree with the contents, opinions, or statements expressed.

List of credits on Acknowledgments page beginning on 188.

ISBN 1-56077-772-9

Faith: Developing an Adult Spirituality

Contents

iii

iv

Faith: Developing an Adult Spirituality

Part 7. Growing in Relationship with Jesus

Part 8. Models of Spirituality

Part 9. Stumbling Blocks

Part 10. Ongoing Formation

vi

Introduction

Belief in God can be risky because it involves placing our trust in a reality—what has been called "the ground of all being"—that we have never seen and that many people in society want us to believe has never existed. But for those who choose to take the risk, belief in God is what ultimately gives our life meaning.

It is important for believers to remember that God is not just another being, *just* bigger and better than everything else. God is the source of all being, the origin, the sustainer, the ground of all that exists. Nothing that exists, exists apart from God.

What should we believe? Why should we believe it? How should we act based on this belief? These are the core questions of an adult Christian. Asking the questions and taking the time to discover the answers—that is what this course is all about. As a senior in high school, you are no doubt faced with many questions about your future. Part of what you will need to discern is where God is going to fit into that picture. This course is going to ask some tough questions. It will also demand honest answers. The goal is for you to decide what you (not your parents or teachers) believe about God and how you can best live out that belief.

vii

Faith

Where is faith found?
Not in a book,
or in a church,
not often or
for everyone.
In childish times
it's easier;
a child believes
just what it's told.
But children grow
and soon begin
to see too much
that doesn't match
the simple tales,
and not enough
of what's behind
their parents' words.
There is no God,
the cynics say;
we made Him up
out of our need
and fear of death.
And happily
they offer up
their test-tube proofs.
A mystery,
the priests all say,
and point to saints
who prove their faith
in acts of love
and sacrifice.

But what of us
who are not saints,
only common
human sinners?
And what of those
who in their need
and pain cry out
to God and go
on suffering?
I do not know—
I wish I did.
Sometimes I feel
all the world's pain.
I only say
that once in my
own need I felt
a light and warm
and loving touch
that eased my soul
and banished doubt
and let me go
on to the end.
It is not proof—
there can be none.
Faith's what you find
When you're alone
And find you're not.[1]

---

[1]Terry A. Anderson, "Faith," in *Den of Lions: Memoirs of Seven Years* (New York: Crown Publishers, Inc., 1993), 98–99. Anderson—then the chief Mideast correspondent for the Associated Press—was abducted in Beirut, Lebanon, by Shiite militants in March 1985 and held hostage until December 1991.

Faith: Developing an Adult Spirituality

Part 1

What Is Faith?

At the beginning of his great letter to the Romans, St. Paul declared his mission to bring to faith those called to belong to Christ (*1:5–6*). That is also the mission of this course.

Faith gives human life meaning. Christian faith involves a commitment of our entire being to God who is revealed to us in Jesus Christ. In this first section, we will examine faith and belief.

2

What I Believe

Part A.

Directions: Faith is an important part of our lives. Faith is ultimately about believing in God. But we also speak about believing in our family and our friends, believing in our school and our country, believing in ourselves. Complete each of the following sentences. Think before you write, and be prepared to share your answers. There are no right or wrong answers.

1.   I believe God

2.   I believe Jesus

3.   I believe the Church

4.   I believe my friends

5.   I believe my family

6.   I believe I

7.   I believe this school

8.   I believe this country

9.   I believe the world would be better if

10. I believe some day

> *We can believe what we choose.*
>
> *We are answerable for what we choose to believe.*
>
> *—Cardinal Newman*

3

Part B.

Directions: Discuss the following questions. Record your answers in the space provided.

1. Have you always believed what you answered in part A? How might your answers have been different five years ago?

2. What has helped you to determine your beliefs? How have your beliefs been formed?

3. Have you ever questioned or doubted any of your beliefs? Explain your answer.

4. Do your beliefs have any influence upon your personal behavior? (For example, if you believe that your parents trust you, do you act in a particular way to keep that trust?)

4

What I Really Believe

Directions: Read the following. Then reread your answers to **Exercise 1**, part A. Determine which of your beliefs require conviction, commitment, and/or trust. List the beliefs under the proper heading.

Adult faith requires conviction, commitment, and trust. Conviction is an action or deep belief that the whole truth that God has revealed is The Truth. Commitment is the pledging of oneself to the long and exacting work of self-mastery and the role of disciple and witness to Christ. Trust is putting oneself confidently into the hands of God for whatever concerns the future and giving up all unhealthy curiosity about it.

1. Beliefs that require conviction

2. Beliefs that require commitment

3. Beliefs that require trust

There are two ways to slide easily through life: to believe everything or to doubt everything. Both ways save us from thinking.

—Alfred Korzybski

5

Where I Am

Thomas answered and said to him, "My Lord and my God!" Jesus said to him, "Have you come to believe because you have seen me? Blessed are those who have not seen and have believed."

—John 20:28-29

Directions: Think carefully about the differences between belief as what we believe *about* someone or something, and faith as freely and honestly believing *in* another. Then review your answers to **Exercises 1** and **2**, and answer the following questions.

1. In your responses to **Exercises 1** and **2**, do you include more faith statements or more belief statements?

2. Do you know more about God, or do you have more faith in God? Why do you think this is so?

3. What topics would you like to see covered to help you know more about God?

4. What do you need from this class to help your faith in God to grow and develop?

Faith Walk

Directions: Faith is a gift of God's loving grace to us, and it is also our free response to God's gift. God doesn't make us believe or love, so faith involves taking risks. You experienced some of those risks in your faith walk. Answer the following questions. Then discuss your answers with your partner.

1. What feelings did you experience as the leader? as the follower?

2. Which role did you like better? Why?

3. As the leader, did you ever break your partner's trust by placing him or her in danger? Why or why not? As the follower, did you ever break your partner's trust by peeking during the walk? Why or why not?

4. Did your prior relationship with your partner make it easier or harder for you to place your trust in him or her?

5. Did your ability to trust your partner change as the walk went on? Explain your answer.

6. How is faith in God like the faith walk exercise?

Faith is to believe what we do not see, and the reward of faith is to see what we believe.

—St. Augustine

7

When You Say Jump, I'll Ask How High

Directions: Read the following statements. Then reflect on the questions and record your responses.

As trust builds, we are willing to say and do many things for those we trust. With faith, there is a degree of certainty that the one in whom we believe is worthy of our trust.

1. In the second faith walk, the volunteer was faced with numerous obstacles. Do you believe that God removes obstacles from our journey in faith?

2. Are we always aware that the obstacles have been removed?

3. Can obstacles in our path ever be considered to be a good thing? Explain.

4. At the end of the second walk, the student was directed to jump over the last obstacle. Have you ever needed to make a leap of faith? Describe the situation.

5. What, if anything, would make trusting God easier?

What Is Faith?

Images of Faith in the Scriptures

Directions: The Bible gives us many outstanding examples of faith. We find persons who assented to God's truth, trusted that God would care for them, demonstrated their faith in various ways by their lives, and proved loyal to God through difficult times. Read the following scriptural passages. Then indicate which dimensions of faith are exemplified in the situations. There can be more than one correct answer. Be prepared to explain your answer.

Choose from the following:

- Intellectual assent to truth
- Personal response of trust in another
- Faithfulness in action
- Loyalty to another in times of difficulty

1. Abraham

   a. *Genesis 12:1–9*   Abraham leaves his home for the land promised to him by God.

   b. *Genesis 22:1–19*   Abraham's faith is tested.

2. Moses

   a. *Exodus 3:4–15*   Moses is commissioned by God.

   b. *Exodus 33:1–17*   Moses becomes intimate with God.

3. David and Jonathan

   a. *1 Samuel 18:1–5*   David and Jonathan become friends.

   b. *1 Samuel 20:11–34*   Jonathan learns of Saul's plot.

4. Mary

   a. *Luke 1:26–38*   Mary experiences the Annunciation.

   b. *John 19:25–30*   Jesus is crucified.

5. Mary and Martha

   a. *John 11:17–27*   Martha confesses her faith.

[I]f you have faith the size of a mustard seed . . .

—Matthew 17:20

9

The Light of Faith

Directions: Read the following statements about light. Slowly and thoughtfully read the reflections on Scripture. Then answer the questions.

Light is a common symbol or metaphor for faith. Like a light, faith illumines the reality of God for us, and lights up the way for us to respond to God in trusting and loyal action.

Consider this passage from Isaiah:

> This, rather, is the fasting that I wish:
>> releasing those bound unjustly,
>> untying the thongs of the yoke;
> Setting free the oppressed,
>> breaking every yoke;
> Sharing your bread with the hungry,
>> sheltering the oppressed and the homeless;
> Clothing the naked when you see them,
>> and not turning your back on your own.
>
> *—Isaiah 58:6–7*

> If you bestow your bread on the hungry
>> and satisfy the afflicted;
> Then light shall rise for you in the darkness,
>> and the gloom shall become for you like
>> midday . . .
>
> *—Isaiah 58:10*

This image of "a light shining in the darkness" is a frequent theme in Scripture. In Genesis, light is the first thing created to bring order to chaos (*Genesis 1:1–3*). God speaks to Moses through a burning bush and leads the people with a pillar of fire (*Exodus 3:2, 13:21–22*). David, the youngest of Jesse's many strong sons, is chosen to be king not because of his outward appearance, but because of what shines forth from his heart—innocence, integrity, and justice. Isaiah reminds us that the people who walked in darkness have seen a great light (*Isaiah 9:2*). Kings follow a star to find Light personified—Jesus the Christ (*Matthew 2:1–12*). Jesus speaks to Nicodemus at night and illuminates for him the miracle of rebirth (*John 3*). Jesus calls himself the Light of the World (*John 8:12*) and challenges us to become light for others (*Matthew 5:14–16*). All four Gospels witness to the fact that not even the darkness of death can extinguish the Light of Christ. The author of the letter to the Ephesians calls us to live as children of the Light—a poignant reminder of Paul's journey from darkness to light. This is Good News indeed!

It is John's Gospel, however, which is the most revealing. It includes the story of a man born blind who, after a little mud in his eye, is able to see The Light. The man's statements about Jesus reflect his growing awareness of God in his life:

> "The man called Jesus . . ." (*9:11*)
>
> "He is a prophet." (*9:17*)
>
> "If this man were not from God . . ." (*9:33*)
>
> "I do believe, Lord . . ." (*9:38*)

What can we learn from this? Growth in faith is a slow and steady process. Although the man born blind is given light in one moment (as we are baptized in one instant), the awareness of the meaning of "light" in his life comes over a period of time. In a similar way, our awareness of the meaning of The Light in our lives grows with time.

In *To Live Is to Love*, Ernesto Cardenal says,

> If in everything you fulfill God's will rather than your own, every encounter in the street, every telephone call, every letter you receive, will be full of meaning, and you will find that everything has its good reason and obeys a providential design.[1]

Suddenly, the light dawns—life has an ultimate meaning. Every human encounter speaks to us of our faith in God.

1. Where does faith come from? How does it originate? (*Note*: Faith in God is not the same as knowledge about God.)

2. What has been the most helpful to you in "seeing the light" about Jesus Christ?

3. Do you agree or disagree that every human encounter speaks to us of our faith in God? Explain your answer.

4. How would this world be different if all eyes were open to the presence of God in every person?

---

[1]Ernesto Cardenal, *To Live Is to Love,* trans. Kurt Reinhardt (New York: Herder and Herder, 1972), 118.

God Calls—How Do I Respond?

Directions: Faith is our free, human response to the revelation of God's loving call to us. How well does your personal faith compare to the faith of the figures in the Bible? Read each of the following passages. Then choose which one is your favorite, and answer the questions.

a. *Deuteronomy 6:5–8*   e. *Jeremiah 31:3*

b. *Psalm 86:15*   f. *Ezekiel 36:26*

c. *Psalm 103:8–10*   g. *Hosea 11:1–4*

d. *Isaiah 49:14–15*

1. Which passage did you select as your favorite? Why?

God does not ask perfect work but infinite desires.

—St. Catherine

12

2. Which dimension of faith (intellectual assent to truth, personal response of trust in another, faithfulness in action, loyalty to another in times of difficulty) does this passage call you to practice? Why?

3. Do you think God places faith in us? Explain your answer.

"Father"—Timothy P. Schmalz

Part 2

Faith Development

Our faith in God grows and matures over time. Modern scholarship shows that this growing process follows a pattern. Once we identify the pattern, we can look for ways to ease our transition from a childish to an adult spirituality.

Spiritual Autobiography

Directions: Spirituality involves how we live out our relationship with God. As you approach this semester, it is helpful to know where you are in your relationship with God and in your faith. To expand your self-knowledge and to allow your teacher to get to know you and your religious self, you are asked to write your religious story. A religious story is about you and your relationship with your God. This exercise will help you to recognize your own growth and development in faith.

Parts of your religious story are very personal and private. What you share will be a matter of strict confidentiality between you and your teacher. This confidentiality is guaranteed so that you can be honest about yourself as you see yourself today. There are no right or wrong answers.

Your story will probably include the following areas:

Background

- What is your religious tradition? (Catholic, Baptist, Lutheran . . .)
- To what parish or church do you belong?
- What have been the major influences on your religious life? (parents, family, friends, teachers, priests, religious tradition . . .) Explain how they influenced you.
- What sort of religious education have you had?
- What faith experiences have you had that have had a significant impact on your spiritual growth?

Relationship with God

- Describe your relationship with God.
- How have you experienced the person of Jesus?
- How does your belief in Jesus affect the way you treat yourself?

Living the Relationship

- How does being a Christian affect your relationships with family, friends, enemies, strangers? Be specific.
- How does your Christian faith affect your decision making?
- Describe the role of prayer in your life. (Do you pray? How? When?)
- Describe how you practice your religion.

Questions or Problems

- What problems or questions do you have with God?
- What problems or questions do you have regarding the Church?

> *What I am to be, I am now becoming.*

15

Westerhoff's Styles of Faith

Directions: Examine the following description of the process of growing in faith. Then answer the questions.

John Westerhoff, a religious educator, uses the cross section of a tree trunk to illustrate the process of faith development. As a tree develops new rings through the years, so too does faith develop a variety of stages over time as a person matures. Each stage encompasses and builds upon the previous stage.

16

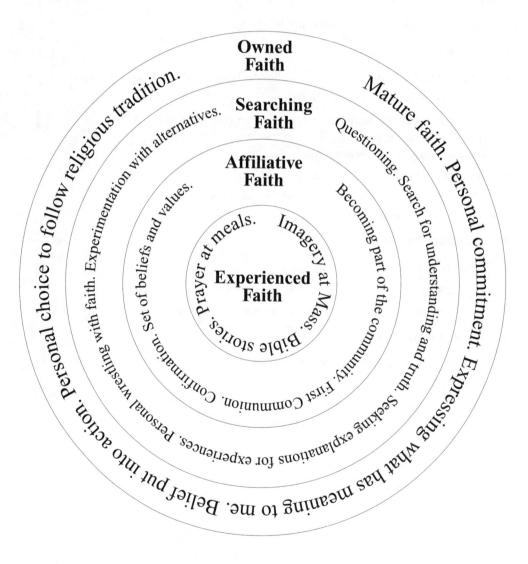

1. What style of faith best exemplifies the faith that you have right now?

2. How long has this been your style?

3. Can you recall what happened to change your faith?

Fowler's Theory of Faith Development

Directions: Read the following information.

Theologian James W. Fowler interviewed more than five hundred people in a process of developing his theory of faith development. He proposes a theory of stages of faith, declaring that faith is a process of becoming rather than a commodity which people possess. He distinguishes six stages that people can go through in their faith journey.

Stage 1: Intuitive-Projective Faith

- Pre-school children, age 0–6
- Children develop basic feelings or intuitions about God, Jesus, and the Church (e.g., seeing God as a loving parent or as a harsh disciplinarian).
- Symbols and images are important. The child may mix fact and fantasy and confuse the sequential pattern of historical events.
- Children reflect the faith of parents and family, the sources of religious authority and information.
- The child understands faith through the family's experience.

Stage 2: Mythic-Literal Faith

- About age 6 to 11 or 12
- Beliefs and understanding come from a wider circle of parent substitutes, such as teachers, older friends, and clergy.
- Children learn stories of faith, for example, the Jesus story.
- Interpretations of the Bible are literal; there is no understanding of deeper symbolism.
- Children at this stage cannot think abstractly; they can only understand things on a concrete level.
- Children become aware that there are different ways of understanding faith. For example, Catholics and Protestants have different approaches.

Stage 3: Synthetic-Conventional Faith

- From about age 12, sometimes through adulthood
- This stage is concerned with the interpersonal need for approval by peers.
- "Unity by uniformity"—harmony, agreement, and conformity are important.
- The person emphasizes creeds, practices, and doctrines that provide identity and a perception of belonging as members of a church.
- The person uses the views of significant others in developing a set of personal values.
- Security is found in a community of like-minded people who share a common faith identity.

There lives more faith in honest doubt, believe me, than in half the creeds.

—Alfred, Lord Tennyson

18

Stage 4: Individuative-Projective Faith

- May begin in late teens or early adulthood, yet can occur anywhere in adult life

- The person focuses on taking responsibility as an adult for one's own commitments and belief system.

- Doubt, questioning, struggling with new concepts, and rejection of traditional assumptions are typical.

- The process of reappraisal is an essential step for faith maturation.

- This stage is temporary; its intensity keeps it from being prolonged.

- It may result in a personal conversion experience.

- It can also have other results—untraditional forms—cult membership, rejection of faith, or atheism.

- People at Stage 4 have a tendency to see one personal model as the only legitimate or meaningful model.

Stage 5: Conjunctive Faith

- A mature faith which many people never reach, rarely found before age 30

- The person recognizes the legitimacy and integrity of other models besides one's own.

- The person often looks at opposite models as sources of growth into deeper knowledge of self. He or she rethinks Stage 4 thinking in light of new awareness. For example, a social activist may explore the contemplative tradition.

- This stage can be expressed in a variety of different ways.

- One integrates childhood teaching and adult issues. Personal faith, traditional approaches, and others' positions come into meaningful unity.

- Commitment to political and moral values deepens.

Stage 6: Universalizing Faith

- Exceedingly rare; the vast majority of people never attain this stage

- Many models work together in perfect harmony.

- The person goes beyond beliefs or a way of living to total, unswerving commitment to the will of God.

- One's focus shifts from one's own needs to selfless service to the human community.

- This stage is characterized by a passionate commitment to life and justice.

- A person is motivated by the guidance of a Supreme Authority.

Faith Development

- Faith takes on a mystical quality.

- This is a prophetic model of faith.

- Examples may include St. Paul, St. Francis of Assisi, Gandhi, Dag Hammarskjold, Martin Luther King Jr., Oscar Romero, and Mother Teresa.

Additional Considerations

- Fowler's stages are hierarchical (increasing in complexity).

- The stages are sequential; people do not skip stages, since each builds on the understandings developed in the previous stage.

- The stages are invariant; they follow the same order for all people.

- Each person finds the stage which has the most personal meaning.

- Stage 3 is the most common stage.

- Some adults never progress beyond Stage 2 or Stage 3.

- In the first three stages, faith comes from an external force; in the last three stages, faith is internal—one takes personal responsibility for one's own faith experience.

- The shift from Stage 3 to Stage 4 is the hardest because one goes from an external to an internal motivation.

- A person can understand the next stage above his or her own stage, but never beyond that.

Source: James W. Fowler, *Stages of Faith: The Psychology of Human Development and the Quest for Meaning* (San Francisco: HarperSanFrancisco, 1995).

Faith Development

Pictograph Activity on Faith

Directions: Using separate paper, create a pictograph of symbols, images, or drawings that will help you to think about and discuss the following reflections. Do not worry about your artistic abilities; the reflection part is the focus.

Reflect on the following dimensions of your life:

- What does faith mean to you?

- What is your earliest faith memory?

- What is your favorite story of faith?

- What helped you to feel part of the Church?

- Who have been the most significant influences on your faith?

- What event helped you to grow most fully in your faith?

- What event most harmed or challenged your faith?

- What is your greatest doubt or question regarding faith?

- What image would best describe where you are currently in regard to faith?

Any work of art is great because it creates a special world of its own.

—Leonard Bernstein

21

You Are Not Alone

> The saints are the sinners who keep on trying.
>
> —Robert Louis Stevenson

22

Part A.

Directions: For many people, faith is something that is personal and private. They rarely have opportunities to hear others talk about their struggles, questions, and doubts regarding faith. However, according to both John Westerhoff and James W. Fowler, this questioning is a prerequisite for moving toward personally owned faith. If you were to read about some of the great religious figures of history—e.g., St. Augustine, St. Theresa of Avila, Thomas Merton, Oscar Romero—you would see that many of them dealt with these issues and challenged established religious practices. Scripture also provides numerous examples of individuals who are held up as models of faith but who nevertheless had to deal with doubts. Read the following passages, and briefly summarize the nature of the doubts reflected in each account.

1. *Genesis 18:1–15*

2. *Exodus 3:1–14*

3. *Exodus 4:1–17*

4. *Job 30:20–31*

5. *Jeremiah 1:4–6*

23

6. *John 20:24–29*

7. *Acts 9:10–16*

Part B.

Directions: Answer the following questions.

1. Which of the passages from part A can you best relate? Explain why.

2. How does the recognition that even powerful religious figures experienced doubts make you feel? Explain your answer.

Keep the Faith

Part A.

Directions: Rank the following statements from 1 to 4 with 1 being closest to your view of faith and 4 being the farthest.

Faith is . . .

_____ a set of beliefs

_____ membership in a church

_____ finding meaning in life

_____ a relationship with God

Write a brief paragraph explaining why you ranked the statements in the order you did.

We seldom lose our faith by a blowout. Usually it is just a slow leak.

–V. Garry

25

Part B.

Directions: Crisis is a part of life. A crisis can be defined as an experience of radical change or a significant turning point. Crisis can be either positive or negative. Research has shown that a crisis can become the catalyst for faith development as a person seeks to make sense of a period of turmoil and to understand how God fits into the experience. Write a checkmark next to the crises that you have experienced. Put a star next to those that you feel have had an effect on your faith development. Feel free to add any additional crises you have faced.

_____ the birth of a sibling

_____ changing schools

_____ moving from familiar surroundings

_____ loss of a friendship

_____ breaking up with a boyfriend or girlfriend

_____ death of a loved one

_____ parents' divorce

_____ parents' remarriage

_____ questions about God or faith

_____ failing a course

_____ starting a new job

_____ serious personal illness

_____ serious illness of a family member

_____ getting arrested

_____ severe financial difficulties

_____ applying to a college

1. Describe one of these experiences and how it affected your faith development.

2. Do you see any predictable crisis in your immediate future? How can your faith help you to deal with this crisis? Explain your answers.

Part C.

Directions: In speaking about their faith, people can describe themselves as religious or as spiritual. Being religious is generally conceived of as involving ritual practices, belief in dogma, active participation in a parish, and following the practices and teaching of the institutional Church. Being spiritual emphasizes the personal dimension, in which a person finds nurturing and growth through forms such as talking with friends, meditation, nature, or music, usually outside of a church setting.

1. Which of these two terms best describes you? Why?

2. Describe someone you know whom you believe could be described as religious.

3. Describe someone you know whom you would consider spiritual.

4. What do you believe is the essential difference between these two people?

5. Do you believe a person can be both religious and spiritual? Why

6. In what sense is the distinction between being religious and being spiritual misleading?

The Rite of Christian Initiation of Adults

> Most people come to religion for what they can get. But we learn religion to learn selflessness— to be righteous regardless of whether we get rewards.
>
> —Mokyrai Cherlin

Part A.

Directions: The Rite of Christian Initiation of Adults, or RCIA, is the model for the journey of faith in the Catholic Church. The journey includes four periods of faith development and three steps of liturgical rituals. The Church as community of faith plays an active role in the process of the RCIA. Christian faith lives and grows in the context of the community of faith as the journey of faith in the RCIA culminates in the sacramental celebration of Baptism, Confirmation, and Eucharist. Read and study the outline of the RCIA.

1. **Period of Evangelization**
   - The Gospel is proclaimed.
   - The community of faith gives witness to the value of faith in their personal lives.
   - Faith is awakened by the Holy Spirit in persons who become sympathizers or inquirers.
   - There is no determined time limit or structure.

2. **Liturgical Step: Acceptance into the Catechumenate**
   - The whole church is invited to celebrate.
   - as a sympathizer or inquirer takes the step to become a Christian catechumen

3. **Period of the Catechumenate**
   - one to several years
   - Catechumens receive catechesis, or instruction on the faith.
   - Catechesis echoes the Gospel, especially as proclaimed throughout the liturgical year.
   - Faith life is deepened through prayer, practicing love of neighbor, giving personal witness.
   - Suitable minor liturgical rites accompany, including celebrations of God's word, minor exorcisms, anointings, and blessings.
   - The community of faith watches over and cares for the catechumens.

4. **Liturgical Step: Election and Enrollment of Names**
   - Catechumens who are prepared are elected to sacramental initiation.
   - They inscribe their names.
   - can be celebrated by the bishop in the diocesan cathedral with catechumens from the diocese

5. **Period of Purification and Enlightenment**
   - corresponds to the season of Lent
   - The elect undergo spiritual recollection to be purified and enlightened.
   - Their faith is consecrated for reception of the Sacraments of Initiation.
   - The community of faith celebrates with the elect the liturgical ritual of Scrutinies, which emphasize self-searching and repentance.
   - The elect are presented with the Creed and Lord's Prayer in liturgical ceremony.

6. **Liturgical Step: Sacraments of Initiation**
   - reception of Baptism, Confirmation, and Eucharist
   - at the Easter Vigil, as the whole community of faith celebrates the Paschal Mystery
   - culminates the journey of faith toward full church membership

7. **Period of Mystagogia**
   - corresponds to the season of Easter
   - deepening grasp of the Paschal Mystery
   - reflection on the experience of having been baptized and confirmed into the eucharistic community
   - continued experience of living the faith and reflecting on its value, prayer and receiving the Eucharist, charity and service

Part B.

Directions: Faith is a journey of steps and stages, crises and turning points, raising questions and overcoming doubts, interacting with others and deciding where one stands, accepting the grace of God and answering with the commitment of one's life. Answer the following questions thoughtfully.

1. Do you think being a person of faith requires an adult commitment? Why or why not?

2. Are you ready to make that adult commitment? Why or why not?

3. Who has been the one person in your life who has helped you become a person of faith?

4. How do you witness your faith to those around you? What more could you do?

Part **3**

Ultimate Questions

Who? What? When? Where? Why? Good reporters know these questions unlock the essential information for a news story. These same questions reveal to us who we are, what our purpose in life is, and how we can make sense out of the human condition.

Erik Erikson's
Theory of Psychological Development

Directions: Erik Erikson, a renowned psychologist, crafted a theory of how human beings grow and mature psychologically in stages. Rather than growing in a straight line that gradually rises, we tend to grow in incremental steps or stages. We rise to a new stage or level as we accomplish an important developmental task or crisis. Then we level off until the next task or crisis comes along. Understanding Erikson's theory can help us to understand how we mature as persons, how we are able as we mature to form more lasting relationships, and how we grow in faith. Carefully read the following summary of Erikson's stages.

Stage 1: Trust vs. Mistrust

- task of early infancy
- involves developing a sense of trust of self, others, and the world
- coming to a belief that one's basic needs will be met
- developing a belief in the basic goodness of people and that life is worthwhile

Stage 2: Autonomy vs. Shame and Doubt

- task of late infancy
- developing of the child's ability to exercise his or her own will
- learning to act independently
- growing in a sense of one's capabilities

Stage 3: Initiative vs. Guilt

- task of early childhood
- learning from experience how life is and how one can affect it
- developing ambition, motivation, and a sense of adventure as a result of initial successes
- learning the skills of problem solving

Stage 4: Industry vs. Inferiority

- task of middle childhood
- a personal sense of worth growing from skill development
- developing a sense of accomplishment, which encourages further productivity
- creating excitement about learning and a desire to complete tasks

Stage 5: Identity vs. Identity Confusion

- task of adolescence
- coming to an understanding of one's unique individuality
- forming one's basic values and attitudes
- looking at what one wants from life and what one has to offer
- seeking to integrate self-concept with the ways one is perceived by others

Youth is the time of life when people are too old to take advice.

Stage 6: Intimacy vs. Isolation

- task of early adulthood
- knowing who one is, seeking to share that self with others in a meaningful relationship, in the work world, in the community
- developing a capacity to share with others
- seeking relationships in which one can share thoughts and feelings
- discovering who wants to be with me and how I will share and commit myself to meaningful others

Stage 7: Generativity vs. Stagnation

- task of middle adulthood
- spanning the major portion of adult life
- extending concern beyond self and one's family
- passing on one's skills to the next generation
- occurring in parenting, passing on experience to young coworkers through apprenticeship or mentoring, leadership through service to others
- seeking to create a better world for the next generation

Stage 8: Ego vs. Integrity and Despair

- period of late adulthood
- involving reflection and appraisal of one's life asking what it all means
- accepting responsibility for what one has made of life
- feeling satisfaction with one's life, work, and achievement

Other Considerations

- Each stage can have either a favorable or an unfavorable resolution.
- The stages are chronologically determined. One cannot skip a stage.
- While people deal with these issues in all stages, there is a proper sequence and period during which they concentrate on a particular task.
- Each stage helps the individual to develop resources necessary to go on to the next task.
- Unsuccessful resolution of the task at one stage inhibits one's ability to deal with the next stage.
- The resolution of each stage helps to form personality.
- No task is ever fully completed.
- People go through the stages with varying degrees of intensity and speed.

Who Am I?

Part A.

Directions: Each block of the Johari Window represents a different dimension of who we are. Listen to your teacher's explanation of how the Johari Window helps us to understand our identity.

The Johari Window

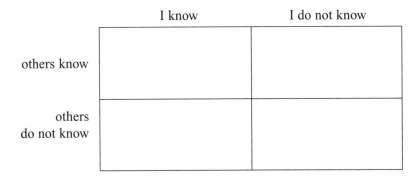

	I know	I do not know
others know		
others do not know		

Part B.

Directions: Examine the following illustration. Consider the difference between self-concept and true self. Be prepared to suggest ways that these two areas can be brought together, that the overlap can be increased.

Self-Concept vs. True Self

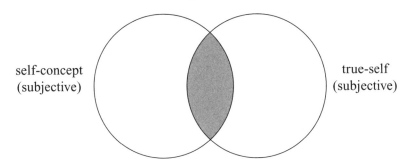

self-concept (subjective)   true-self (subjective)

These understandings can be brought together by

1.

2.

3.

We may well go to the moon, but that's not very far. The greatest distance we have to cover still lies within us.

—Charles De Gaulle

35

Part C.

Directions: Write ten answers to the "Who Am I" question. Be prepared to share your responses.

1. I am

2. I am

3. I am

4. I am

5. I am

6. I am

7. I am

8. I am

9. I am

10. I am

Who Does God Say I Am?

Directions: Our family, peers, and culture all give us messages about our identity. Our self-concept is formed by this information. At times, though, these messages may be distorted, inaccurate, or misunderstood. To know who we truly are, we need to find an objective standard which will help us to evaluate how correct these messages are. Our God tells us who he created us to be. Read the following scriptural passages, and note the truth revealed about who you are according to God's revelation. Then write a paragraph on how you feel about what God says about you in these Scriptures and how this message compares to other messages you have received from people around you.

1. *Genesis 1:27*

2. *Genesis 1:31*

3. *Isaiah 43:4*

4. *Matthew 6:26*

5. *John 15:15*

6. *John 15:16*

7. *Romans 8:14–17*

8. *1 Peter 2:9*

Every individual is a miracle.

—Antoine de Saint-Exupéry

37

A Model for Discernment

Directions: Examine the following explanation of a prayerful approach to discover God's will in our lives.

In the days of sailing ships, there was a beautiful harbor which was the major port for a coastal city. The harbor was essential to the city's economic well-being and was ideal in every way but one. There was a problem gaining access to it. Off the coast there were treacherous reefs and sandbars which frequently wrecked ships attempting to sail into the harbor. After many disasters, the city finally discovered a solution which would guarantee safe entry into the harbor. Three lighthouses were built in a direct row which lined up with the safe passage. If all three lighthouses were lined up so that it appeared as if there were only one lighthouse, then a ship would know that it was on a safe course to enter the harbor. However, if an approaching ship could see more than one lighthouse, then it would know that it was in danger and would need to adjust course until all three were lined up one behind the other.

This true story provides a helpful model for when we are seeking God's will regarding a decision in our lives. There are three elements which, if they are in agreement with one another, indicate we are on a correct course. When, however, they are not in agreement, we need to move cautiously, delay making a final decision, and perhaps reconsider what we were contemplating doing.

The three elements we must consider are the following:

1. Is what I am seeking to do compatible with the teaching of Scripture?

2. Am I comfortable with and at peace with the contemplated choice?

3. Does the feedback I receive from others who know me and care about me encourage this choice?

Some people are like boats— they toot loudest when in a fog.

Scripture and God's Purpose for My Life

Directions: Do I believe that God has created me? If God has created me, do I believe that God has a specific purpose for my life? Read the following scriptural passages that point to the direction God has for human life, and answer the questions.

1. Read *2 Timothy 3:15–16*. What does this passage say about the use of Scripture in seeking to understand God's purpose in my life?

2. Read the following passages. What does each one say about God's purpose for our lives?

   a. *John 3:16–17*

   b. *John 10:10b*

   c. *1 Timothy 2:4*

   d. *Matthew 22:34–40*

   e. *Matthew 25:14–30*

3. In what way do the passages from John and Timothy reveal the Good News?

4. How do the passages from Matthew differ from the others?

My business is not to remake myself, but to make the absolute best of what God has made.

—Robert Browning

39

My Obituary

Directions: Dr. Elizabeth Kübler-Ross, a pioneer in research on death and dying, says that when we contemplate death, it forces us to look at what is important in our lives. The purpose of this exercise is to look at what we desire to do with our lives—what types of relationships we desire, what type of work we want, what we hope to accomplish. Project yourself seventy years into the future and write your obituary as you would hope your life to have been looking back at it from that future point. Information in your obituary could include the following items:

- Name and age at time of death
- Cause of death
- Your survivors
- Activities in which you were involved
- Organizations to which you belonged
- Major life accomplishments
- What you hope to be remembered for
- Why people will mourn your death
- What the world lost because of your death
- What arrangements have been made for your funeral
- Any donations that may be made in your name

You cannot control the length of your life, but you can control the depth and height.

40

The Search for Meaning

Directions: Throughout history, great thinkers have pondered the mystery of life. Read the following quotations, and explain what you think each one is trying to say about our human search for meaning.

1. "The unexamined life is not worth living." (Socrates)

2. "The mass of men lead lives of quiet desperation." (Henry David Thoreau)

3. "If we have our own why of life, we shall get along with almost any how." (Friedrich Nietzsche)

4. "Those who have no purpose in life live for kicks." (John Powell, S.J.)

5. "Our hearts are restless, O Lord, until they rest in you." (St. Augustine)

41

Man's Search for Meaning

> *Thus was I learned that Love is our Lord's meaning.*
>
> —Julian of Norwich

Directions: Viktor E. Frankl was a Jewish psychiatrist who survived the horrors of the Nazi concentration camps. After his release he sought to make sense out of this experience and published his reflections in the book *Man's Search for Meaning.* In the book he sought to explain why some survived while others gave up in despair and died. He also saw that some of the people in the camps became self-centered individuals who cared only about their own personal welfare. Their code was the survival of the fittest. Others in the exact same circumstances exhibited great generosity of spirit, comforting others, sharing the little they had, and caring for those worse off than themselves. Frankl sought to explain why people in the same situation ended up so different from one another. Below is an excerpt for reflection and discussion.

In spite of all the enforced physical and mental primitiveness of the life in a concentration camp, it was possible for spiritual life to deepen. Sensitive people who were used to a rich intellectual life may have suffered much pain (they were often of a delicate constitution), but the damage to their inner selves was less. They were able to retreat from their terrible surroundings to a life of inner riches and spiritual freedom. . . . In order to make myself clear, I am forced to fall back on personal experience. Let me tell what happened on those early mornings when we had to march to our work site. . . .

We stumbled on in the darkness, over big stones and through large puddles, along the one road leading from the camp. The accompanying guards kept shouting at us and driving us with the butts of their rifles. Anyone with very sore feet supported himself on his neighbor's arm. Hardly a word was spoken; the icy wind did not encourage talk. Hiding his mouth behind his upturned collar, the man marching next to me whispered suddenly: "If our wives could see us now! I do hope they are better off in their camps and don't know what is happening to us."

That brought thoughts of my own wife to mind. And as we stumbled on for miles, slipping on icy spots, supporting each other time and again, dragging one another up and onward, nothing was said, but we both knew: each of us was thinking of his wife. Occasionally I looked at the sky, where the stars were fading and the pink light of the morning was beginning to spread behind a dark bank of clouds. But my mind clung to my wife's image, imagining it with an uncanny acuteness. I heard her answering me, saw her smile, her frank and encouraging look. Real or

42

not, her look was then more luminous than the sun which was beginning to rise.

A thought transfixed me: for the first time in my life I saw the truth as it is set into song by so many poets, proclaimed as the final wisdom by so many thinkers. The truth—that love is the ultimate and the highest goal to which man can aspire. Then I grasped the meaning of the greatest secret that human poetry and human thought and belief have to impart: *The salvation of man is through love and in love.* I understood how a man who has nothing left in this world still may know bliss, be it only for a brief moment, in the contemplation of his beloved. . . . For the first time in my life I was able to understand the meaning of the words, "The angels are lost in perpetual contemplation of an infinite glory.". . .

My mind still clung to the image of my wife. A thought crossed my mind: I didn't even know if she were still alive. I knew only one thing—which I have learned well by now: Love goes very far beyond the physical person of the beloved. It finds its deepest meaning in his spiritual being, his inner self. Whether or not he is actually present, whether or not he is still alive at all, ceases somehow to be of importance. . . .

Seen from this point of view, the mental reactions of the inmates of a concentration camp must seem more to us than the mere expression of certain physical and sociological conditions. Even though conditions such as lack of sleep, insufficient food and various mental stresses may suggest that the inmates were bound to react in certain ways, in the final analysis it becomes clear that the sort of person the prisoner became was the result of an inner decision, and not the result of camp influences alone. Fundamentally, therefore, any man can, even under such circumstances, decide what will become of him—mentally and spiritually. He may retain his human dignity even in a concentration camp. . . .[1]

43

[1]Viktor E. Frankl, *Man's Search for Meaning: An Introduction to Logotherapy* (Cutchogue, N.Y.: Buccaneer Books, 1992), 47–50, 75.

Signs of God's Existence

God,
come
quickly!

—Psalm 70:6

Directions: Read the following information. Then answer the questions.

Believing in God is difficult. We cannot see God as we can see the person sitting next to us. We live in a scientific world where evidence of something's reality or truth must be demonstrated to our senses. But we have no empirical proof of God, so we wonder if God really exists.

Perhaps there are signs of God's existence around us, very subtle signs that point us in the direction of God's transcendence surrounding us.

1. Have you or anyone you know, like parent or grandparent, ever prayed hard and experienced the prayer being answered? Describe what happened.

2. Have you or anyone you know ever had an experience of being filled with divine grace or light or presence? Describe the experience.

3. Did you ever turn to God in times of crisis or distress? Do you know others who do? Why do people do that?

4. Name some of the people in your life who have tried to pass on their faith to you. In general, do you trust them? Why?

5. Name some of the things you believe in without having physical proof. Are the love of your parents for each other or the trustworthiness of your friends good examples? Explain.

45

6. Compose the best argument you can think of for why God exists.

Old and New Proofs

Directions: Read the paragraph. Then, with the help of your teacher, complete the chart.

Throughout history great thinkers have tried to prove the existence of God. Their efforts have produced insights to God's reality, but the proofs have been inconclusive in showing once and for all that God truly does exist.

Proofs	Insights	Inadequacies
Ontological argument (based on who God is)		
• If God is the greatest		
• Then God exists in reality		

Our God is in heaven; whatever God wills is done.

—*Psalm 115:3*

46

Proofs	Insights	Inadequacies
Cosmological arguments (based on observation of the cosmos)		
• Causality		
• First mover		
• Order		
• Contingency		
• Perfection		

Proofs	Insights	Inadequacies
Pragmatic arguments		
• The wager		
• The watchmaker		
• The millions who have believed		

Proofs	Insights	Inadequacies
Experiential arguments		
• The anthropic principle (evolution has a purpose—to support human life)		
• Fundamental trust		

Only One God?

Directions: Read the following information. Then look up the scriptural passages to determine what each says about the struggle to know the one true God.

The Bible is the story of biblical people's struggle to believe in God. Unlike the scientific world in which we live, their problem was that they lived in a world surrounded by many gods and goddesses. They struggled to know which one of those was the one true, living God, worthy of their trust and their worship. Sometimes they succeeded; often they failed.

1. *Exodus 20:2–6*

2. *Exodus 32:1–6*

3. *Judges 2:10–12*

4. *1 Samuel 8:1–8*

5. *1 Kings 11:4–6*

6. *1 Kings 14:22–24*

7. *Isaiah 46:1–4*

8. *Acts 17:22–31*

9. *Romans 1:20–21*

10. *1 Corinthians 15:12–14*

Worthless are all the false gods of the land.

—Psalm 16:3

50

Less Than Perfect

Part A.

Directions: The experience of evil is the greatest challenge to belief in the existence of God. Check off which of the following three statements you think is true.

_____ God is an all-powerful being who can do anything that God wants to do.

_____ God is all-loving, caring for each and every living creature.

_____ Evil confronts us.

Explain, if you can, what the contradiction is in checking off all three statements.

Part B.

Directions: Some of the evil in the world is physical evil. Make a list of natural disasters and other physical evils. Then answer the questions.

1. Have you or your family ever been personally affected by natural disasters or other physical evils? Explain.

2. Do you think God creates physical evil? Why or why not?

My being thirsts for God, the living God.

When can I go and see the face of God?

—Psalm 42:3

51

Part C.

Directions: Some of the evil in the world is moral evil. Moral evil is the result of evil choices that human beings make. Answer the following questions.

1. Why do you think God made us free?

2. Why do we choose to do evil?

The Problem

Part A.

Directions: Read *Genesis 3:1–24*. Then answer the following questions.

1. Why did the woman choose to eat the fruit?

2. What was the immediate result of the action?

3. After God discovers the disobedience, what do the people do to try to escape the consequences of their actions?

4. What are the consequences of their actions?

5. Many scholars believe that the story of Adam and Eve's fall is essentially a story about growing up. In the story, the innocence of childhood is replaced with the reality of adulthood. Name some of the ways in which your life is more complicated now that you are older. Is it true that ignorance is bliss?

> *The last temptation is the greatest treason: to do the right deed for the wrong reason.*
>
> —T. S. Eliot

53

Part B.

Directions: Read *Psalm 51*. Then answer the following questions.

1. Verse 7 refers to the idea that the psalmist was born in guilt. Catholics view this as a foreshadowing of the doctrine of original sin. Why do we say that original sin is inherited?

2. According to the psalmist, can we earn God's forgiveness? Can we make ourselves righteous?

Part C.

Directions: Read *Romans 5:12–21*. Then answer the following questions.

1. How did death enter the world?

2. What is the gracious gift to which Paul refers?

3. How has life come to all people?

Part D.

Directions: Read *Romans 7:13–25*. Then answer the following questions.

1. What is Paul complaining about?

2. According to Paul, can obedience to the law free us from the effects of sin? In other words, can we earn salvation?

3. Who can free us from the bondage of sin?

56

Part 4

God, the Answer

For believers, God is the answer to every question we have about what ultimately matters. This section examines what the Catholic tradition believes about God and how God is active in the world.

Characteristics of God

Directions: Read the following descriptions of six of God's characteristics. Find a scriptural passage to illustrate each one and answer the Think About It questions.

1. God is *imminent*—God is close to us and intimately involved in our world. Salvation history recounts numerous instances in which God acts decisively to save the nation of Israel and the fledgling Christian community.

    Example:

    Think About It—God is so close to us that we often do not recognize God's presence until after the fact—in hindsight. Describe an instance when this was true in your own life.

2. God is *transcendent*—God is not tied to the limits of time and space. The Scriptures are filled with descriptions of the awe and majesty of our God. God is so far beyond our understanding that we will never be able to exhaust God's activity in the world.

    Example:

    Think About It—We will never be able to understand God completely. What do you consider to be the most "awesome" aspect of God?

They name him Wonder-Counselor, God-Hero, Father-Forever, Prince of Peace.
—Isaiah 9:5

59

3. God is *eternal*—God is without beginning or end. God is the author and giver of all that is and all that will ever be. God is the only constant in the universe, the one and only unchangeable, ever present source of love.

Example:

Think About It—Thomas Aquinas uses the eternal nature of God as the basis for his classical proofs of God's existence. Which of his proofs makes the most sense to you? Explain.

4. God is *omnipotent*—God is all powerful. God has power over the heavens and the earth, over nations and all creatures. More importantly, God has power over sin, life, and death.

Example:

Think About It—Describe a time when you were most aware of the power of God in your life. In what way(s) are you a different person today because of the power of God in your life?

5. God is *omniscient*—God knows all that is and all that will ever be. God knows our needs even before we are aware of them. God knows each one of us both individually and completely.

Example:

Think About It—God knows everything there is to know about you and still loves you beyond all measure. Does this fact make any difference in your life?

6. God is *personal*—God has the qualities and characteristics that we associate with human beings. God is loving, caring, compassionate, and understanding. Moreover, God is both approachable and communicative.

Example:

Think About It—What kinds of things do you share with your friends? God is our best friend. God listens to us and understands our joys and sorrows. Examine your prayer life. What kinds of things do you share with God? What does this indicate about the type of relationship you have with God?

What's Your J.Q.?

Directions: At the center of Christian faith is belief in Jesus Christ. To be a Christian essentially means believing that the one true God is revealed in Jesus Christ. As the Nicene Creed expresses it, "We believe in one Lord, Jesus Christ, the only Son of God." To know Jesus is to know God.

You are probably familiar with I.Q. tests. This is a J.Q. test to survey your understanding of Jesus. Put a check in the column that reflects your responses most accurately.

	Agree	Disagree	Not Sure
1. Jesus was a Jew.	_____	_____	_____
2. Jesus lived most of his life at Nazareth.	_____	_____	_____
3. Jesus was a real human being.	_____	_____	_____
4. Jesus is alive now.	_____	_____	_____
5. Jesus was crucified by Romans.	_____	_____	_____
6. Jesus did not experience human feelings.	_____	_____	_____
7. Jesus healed people of their afflictions.	_____	_____	_____
8. Jesus never had to learn anything.	_____	_____	_____
9. Jesus is the true Son of God.	_____	_____	_____
10. Jesus taught a very strict code of what people should do.	_____	_____	_____
11. Jesus expresses himself now through the Church.	_____	_____	_____
12. Jesus did not really have to die.	_____	_____	_____
13. Jesus is the Messiah.	_____	_____	_____
14. Jesus rose from the dead.	_____	_____	_____
15. Jesus was a good man— but not God.	_____	_____	_____
16. Jesus is my personal savior.	_____	_____	_____
17. Jesus loves me.	_____	_____	_____
18. Jesus can be met now in other people.	_____	_____	_____

62

Titles of Christ

Part A.

Directions: Use the *Catechism of the Catholic Church*, a theological dictionary, Catholic encyclopedia, or Catholic Web site to determine the meaning of the following titles of Jesus Christ. Reflect upon how you relate to Jesus as he is described in each title.

1. Jesus
   Reflect—Do I realize my need for a personal savior?

2. Christ
   Reflect—Do I experience Jesus as set apart, uniquely recognized as the means of my salvation?

3. Savior
   Reflect—Do I live my life as one who has been freed from bondage to sin and death?

4. Lord
   Reflect—Do I serve God alone in all of my thoughts and actions?

5. Rabbi
   Reflect—Do I look to the teachings of Jesus Christ as the source of examples for how I should live my life?

And he asked them, "But who do you say that I am?"

—Mark 8:29

63

God, the Answer

6. Son of David
   Reflect—Do I allow myself to be an instrument of the kingdom of God ushered in through Jesus Christ?

7. Son of Man
   Reflect—Do I see Jesus as the means by which I have become a new creation in God?

8. Son of God
   Reflect—Do I see Jesus Christ as the fullest revelation of God in the world?

9. Lamb of God
   Reflect—Do I appreciate the sacrifice Jesus Christ made for me through his death on the cross?

10. Good Shepherd
    Reflect—Do I allow Jesus Christ to lead and guide me in all my actions?

Part B.

Directions: Respond to the following summary questions.

1. What are the strongest aspects of your faith in Jesus Christ?

2. In which areas do you feel the need to grow?

3. Compose an Act of Faith. Include what you believe about Jesus Christ and what you commit yourself to act upon because of that faith.

The Necessity of Jesus' Death and Resurrection

See, see
where Christ's
blood
streams
in the
firmament.
One drop
would save
my soul,
half a drop,
ah my
Christ.

—Christopher
Marlowe

Directions: It is worth repeating that Christ's death and resurrection are at the core of Christian faith about God. By his death and his constant love for and forgiveness of his persecutors in his suffering, Jesus frees us from sin and reveals the love of God for us. By rising from the dead, he shows us the way to new life in fulfilled happiness with God. Read *1 Corinthians 15*, St. Paul's reflection on the meaning of the Paschal Mystery, Jesus passing over from death to new life. Then answer the following questions.

1. All human beings die. Jesus was truly human. Jesus had to die in order to share fully in our humanity. Does this realization bring you comfort? Explain your answer.

2. According to Paul, why did Jesus die?

3. Paul tells us that without the resurrection, our faith would be in vain. Why?

4. Why does Paul say that we are to be pitied if our hope in Christ is only for this life?

5. The fullest expression of sin is death. Jesus' conquering of death is his ultimate triumph over sin. Explain, then, why both death and resurrection are necessary for our salvation.

God, the Answer

The Stumbling Block

Directions: Meditating on Jesus' redemptive sufferings for us has been an important spiritual exercise throughout Christian tradition. Read the following passage from St. Paul, and answer the questions.

> The message of the cross is foolishness to those who are perishing, but to us who are being saved it is the power of God. For it is written:
>
> "I will destroy the wisdom of the wise,
>   and the learning of the learned I will set
>   aside."
>
> Where is the wise one? Where is the scribe? Where is the debater of this age? Has not God made the wisdom of the world foolish? For since in the wisdom of God the world did not come to know God through wisdom, it was the will of God through the foolishness of the proclamation to save those who have faith. For Jews demand signs and Greeks look for wisdom, *but we proclaim Christ crucified*, a stumbling block to Jews and foolishness to Gentiles, but to those who are called, Jews and Greeks alike, Christ the power of God and the wisdom of God. For the foolishness of God is wiser than human wisdom, and the weakness of God is stronger than human strength.
>
> *—1 Corinthians 1:18–25*, emphasis added

1. Why was crucifixion a terrible way to die? Explain any of the facts of crucifixion that you know.

> Reality has . . . turned out more mysterious than ever before.
>
> —Daniel Stern

67

2. A second-century depiction of a crucifixion in graffiti shows the head of an ass on the body of a crucified man. The caption reads: Alexamenos worships God. Christians faced ridicule for their faith in the risen Jesus. Today, in Western society, Christians do not risk ridicule for their faith. Or do they? Compare the quality of faith the early Christians must have had with the quality of faith expressed in contemporary society. Is there a difference? Why or why not? What can we do to grow in our faith?

3. Wearing a cross around the neck as decorative costume jewelry is an accepted practice among some Western teens and young adults. What do you think of the practice? Does it honor Christ or Christian faith? Why or why not?

4. Jesus' courage in facing death was the result of his self-emptying love for us. Allowing himself to be accused, he identified with everyone who is accused. He suffered because of human evil and in his suffering, he offered mercy and forgiveness. That mercy is our salvation. It is Jesus' gift to us, and it cost Jesus dearly. What are you doing with his gift of salvation?

The Holy Spirit in Scripture

Directions: The Christian concept of God is a Trinity of three divine persons—Father, Son, and Holy Spirit. Christians believe God is a Trinity because of their experience of Jesus. In his sermons, parables, prayers, and especially his death and resurrection, Jesus revealed the love of the one he called the Father for us. Throughout his life, Jesus was filled with the Spirit of God. At Pentecost, the Risen Christ revealed the gift of the Spirit to the believing Church. We see the work of the Spirit throughout the pages of Scripture. Read each passage below. Indicate what role the Spirit plays in each passage. Use the following list as a source.

Creativity

Source of New Life

Prophecy

Wisdom and Right Judgment

Protection

Giver of Gifts

Power

Authority for Ministry

1. *Genesis 1:1–2*

2. *Genesis 2:7*

3. *Genesis 8:1*

4. *Numbers 11:24–25*

5. *Numbers 24:2*

6. *Judges 3:10*

7. *Judges 11:29*

8. *Wisdom 15:11*

9. *Isaiah 11:2*

10. *Mark 1:10–11*

11. *Luke 1:15*

12. *Luke 1:35*

13. *Acts 2:1–4*

14. *Romans 8:14–16*

15. *1 Corinthians 12:4–11*

When you send forth your breath, they are created . . .

—Psalm 104:30

The Role of the Holy Spirit

> And I will ask the Father, and he will give you another Advocate to be with you always . . .
>
> —John 14:16

Directions: Spirituality is our guide to living the new life of the Holy Spirit. The Spirit has many roles in the history of salvation. Using the *Catechism of the Catholic Church*, a theological dictionary, Catholic encyclopedia, or Catholic Web site, research the various aspects of the Spirit's work to answer the following questions.

1. What is the Holy Spirit's role in the inspiration of Scripture?

2. What is the Holy Spirit's role in the Sacraments of Baptism and Confirmation?

3. What are the "fruits of the Holy Spirit"? Why are these fruits important to the Church today? (*Hint*: Check a concordance to determine where this phrase is found in Scripture.)

4. What are the "gifts of the Holy Spirit"? How can these gifts be used in the Church today? (*Hint*: Check a concordance to determine where this phrase is found in Scripture.)

5. How is the Holy Spirit present in the leadership and guidance of the Church today?

God, the Answer

The Spirit in the Church

Directions: The Acts of the Apostles could easily be renamed the acts of the Holy Spirit. After the Spirit was given to the Church on the first Pentecost, the Spirit guides the Church in its growth and mission. The pages of Acts show the Spirit alive as an active presence in the Church. Determine how the Spirit is active in the events described in each of the following passages.

1. *Acts 1:6–11*

2. *Acts 2:1–13*

3. *Acts 2:14–36*

4. *Acts 4:1–22*

5. *Acts 4:23–32*

6. *Acts 7:54–60*

7. *Acts 9:10–19*

8. *Acts 11:1–18*

9. *Acts 19:1–12*

10. *Acts 28:17–30*

If the spirit within us withers, so too will all the world we build around us.

—Theodore Roszak

71

"Christ Washing Peter's Feet"—Timothy P. Schmalz

Part 5

Kingdom of God vs. Kingdom of the World

Jesus Christ calls his disciples to be different from the rest of the world. He says in John's Gospel, "This is how all will know that you are my disciples, if you have love for one another (*13:35*)." The love to which we are called demands a radical change in lifestyle—one that is very different from what the rest of society expects.

The Kingdom of the World

Directions: In the New Testament, two kingdoms are described: the kingdom of the world and the kingdom of God. These two kingdoms are in opposition to one another. The world's ways and God's ways are in opposition. But the worldly kingdom will be overcome by the divine kingdom. God's loving power will triumph over evil, as the Paschal Mystery of Jesus has already revealed. The following scriptural passages divulge the nature of the world's kingdom. Summarize each passage and explain what is revealed about the kingdom of the world.

1. The nature of the world's kingdom

    Matthew 4:8–9

    Mark 8:36

    John 8:23

    John 18:36

    These passages teach

2. The world's teaching

    John 16:8

    1 Corinthians 1:20

    1 Corinthians 3:19

The
straight
and narrow
path would
get a lot
wider if
more people
used it.

—Arnold Morse

75

Philippians 3:19

These passages teach

3. Love of the world
    James 4:4

    1 John 2:15

    These passages teach

4. The ruler of the world
    John 14:20

    John 16:11

    1 John 5:19

    These passages teach

5. Jesus and the world

   John 12:13

   John 16:33

   Revelations 11:15

   These passages teach

6. The future of the world

   1 Corinthians 7:31

   1 John 2:17

   These passages teach

7. The disciples of Jesus and the world

   John 15:19

   John 17:16

Romans 12:2

James 1:27

1 John 5:4

These passages teach

8. The Church's mission to the world
   Matthew 5:14

   Mark 16:15

   John 17:18

   These passages teach

9. The world's response to Christians
   John 15:18

   John 17:14

   These passages teach

The World's Values

Directions: Jesus tells us that the ways of the world are contrary to the ways of God. Sin, at times, causes us to assign too high a value to things that are limited and will come to an end. We may falsely believe that these items, activities, or values are of ultimate importance. In the jumble below, there are twenty common examples. Circle each of the words, which may be vertical, horizontal, diagonal, or backwards.

```
C F D I N D U L G E N C E Y G J M O P
L E C Q I T S E L F I N T E R E S T L
P C O Z S O F D N G P I H E J I N R E
E N M O D E E R F O R O T K H E Y O A
B E P C U B L M S A I R W O M Z P F S
Y D E A Q S R S L T I V U E W X Y M U
T N T F K Z E U S B A H T E R B N O R
U E I K R S P Q U C D I E H K Y J C E
R P T P S O L T C E X C I T E M E N T
U E I I P N I N C S E X S E B O S S U
C D O T A O O W E A L T H F I N V M X
E N N A N B G T S K L X J W J E R G Q
S I C B O E R H S E C U R I T Y R W N
D E D S F L I E C N E I D E P X E Y V
C V Z J M D R U N K E N N E S S W X B
```

boss	expedience	pleasure	security
comfort	freedom	popularity	self-interest
competition	independence	possessions	sex
drunkenness	indulgence	power	success
excitement	money	retribution	wealth

We need a world in which it is safe to be human.

—Arthur Goldberg

79

Promoting the Reign of God

Part A.

Directions: Read the following information.

The authors of the Christian Scriptures use the phrases the kingdom, the kingdom of heaven, and the reign of God interchangeably. No matter which phrase they use, they are referring to the sovereignty of God made manifest in human experience. The reign of God is announced with the ministry of Jesus. What Jesus said and did, his parables and his miracles, his table fellowship, his passion, death, and resurrection describe what the kingdom is like. Jesus' resurrection and sending the Holy Spirit assure that the kingdom will continue through all eternity. Each of us is invited to participate in that reign by our response to Jesus.

Part B.

Directions: Imagine that you are the director of a large advertising firm. The four evangelists and St. Paul all come to you because they have been given the responsibility to proclaim the kingdom of God, and they want you to help them in this task. They leave you some samples of their writing to give you background on the reign of God. You call together your research staff and ask the members to read the material, sift through it, and develop a fact sheet to aid you in developing this campaign.

Read each set of Scriptures, and record facts revealed about the kingdom (reign) of God.

Scriptures	Facts
1. *Matthew 4:17*	
Matthew 12:28	
1 Corinthians 4:20	
Luke 17:20–22	
2. *Matthew 6:10*	
Matthew 13:31–33	
Mark 9:1	
John 18:36	

Kingdom of God vs. Kingdom of the World

Scriptures	Facts
3. *Matthew 7:21*	
Matthew 25:31–40	
John 3:5	
4. *Matthew 19:23–24*	
Matthew 25:41–46	
1 Corinthians 6:9–10	
Galatians 5:19–21	
5. *Matthew 18:1–4*	
Matthew 19:13–15	
Matthew 21:31–32	
James 2:5	
6. *Matthew 13:44*	
Matthew 13:45–46	
7. *Matthew 16:19*	
Luke 9:2	
Luke 10:9–11	

81

Part C.

Directions: After reviewing the facts prepared by your research team, your creative consultants suggest the most effective means of proclaiming the kingdom of God. Design a billboard that would effectively convey this concept to the public.

82

Parables of the Reign of God

Directions: Read the following information about parables. Then read the parables listed in this exercise. Be aware that Jesus spoke to an audience that was primarily an agricultural community. Using your own creativity and imagination, rewrite or compose your own kingdom of God parable that would speak to today's technological, materialistic, information-centered culture.

Parables are short texts and stories that use metaphors and similes to reveal religious truths. Jesus used these word pictures both to instruct and to challenge. He used the parables as a way of making the kingdom of God and its demands something comprehensible to his listeners. His metaphors and similes enabled his audience to move from objects and events with which they were familiar to understand a reality far beyond their experience. Jesus calls for a response from those who hear the parables. Their messages offer an implicit invitation to a change of attitude or conduct.

Matthew 13:44–46	the parable of the treasure and the pearl
Matthew 13:47–50	the parable of the net
Matthew 20:1–16	the parable of the laborers in the vineyard
Matthew 22:1–14	the parable of the wedding banquet
Matthew 25:1–13	the parable of the ten virgins
Matthew 25:14–30	the parable of the silver pieces
Luke 13:18–19	the parable of the mustard seed
Luke 13:20–21	the parable of the yeast

"Do you understand all these things?"

—Matthew 13:51

83

My Hero!

Those who stand for nothing will fall for anything.

Directions: Most people have heroes, people we admire, look up to, try to imitate. For Christians, Jesus can be that hero. Use the following points to reflect on your understanding of what it means to be a hero.

1. Heroes are people we admire because of their traits or their accomplishments. Name one of your personal heroes, and explain why you consider that person heroic.

2. Ted Tollefson, a minister in Minneapolis, describes a number of criteria for a hero. Explain how your hero meets these characteristics:

   • A hero does something worth talking about.

   • A hero serves powers or principles larger than self.

   • A hero lives a life worthy of imitation.

   • A hero is a catalyst for change.

3. What is the difference between a hero and a celebrity?

4. Which is more heroic—to perform an act of heroism in a crisis situation or to persist in doing something difficult in the face of opposition? Explain your answer.

5. How is Jesus a hero?

6. Name other Christian heroes, and explain why they can be considered heroic.

7. Name someone you know personally who comes closest to being a Christian hero. Explain why this person leads a heroic life.

8. Could you, yourself, be considered a Christian hero? Why or why not?

Kingdom Values

Directions: Jesus proclaims that the kingdom of God is at hand. Those who experience the kingdom are those who have submitted their lives to God's reign by accepting his will for their lives. As the Holy Spirit works in our lives to bring us into conformity with God's will, we find our values and priorities changing. God is making us into a new creation in the image of his son, Jesus. The Scriptures describe various qualities and characteristics that are exhibited by those who are Jesus' disciples. We find that these reflect values that stand in radical contrast to the world's values. In order to identify these values, use the clues to complete the crossword puzzle. To aid in your search, each clue notes a scriptural verse that contains the word needed to complete the puzzle. The clues are based on the *New American Bible* translation, which you will need to complete the puzzle easily.

86

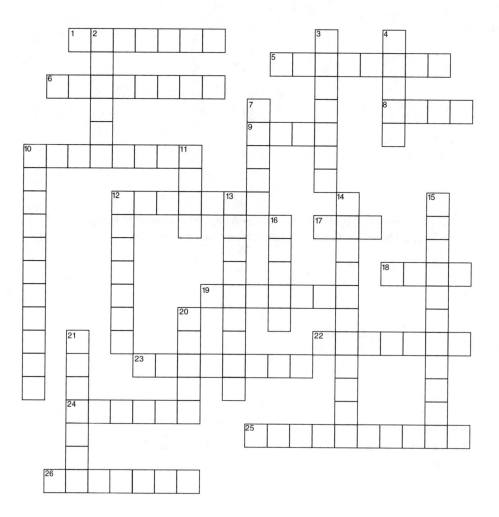

Across

1. giving aid or assistance to the poor (*Acts 9:36*)
5. virtue, moral soundness (*Titus 1:8*)
6. being sympathetic or benevolent (*Colossians 3:12*)
8. to be attentive to another's needs (*Titus 3:14*)
9. confidence or desire for the future (*Romans 8:24*)
10. speaking honestly (*1 Timothy 3:8*)
12. providing aid or a time of duty (*Ephesians 6:7*)
17. happiness or bliss (*John 15:11*)
18. the opposite of death (*John 10:10*)
19. insuring moral fairness (*Romans 3:21*)
22. persevering, waiting without complaint (*1 Corinthians 13:4*)
23. purity or celibacy (*Galatians 5:23*)
24. treating others with tenderness (*1 Timothy 6:11*)
25. being faithful in the performance of duty (*Matthew 25:21*)
26. treating another with dignity (*Romans 12:10*)

Down

2. upright, truthful (*Philippians 4:8*)
3. interest, caring (*2 Corinthians 8:7*)
4. granting pardon, compassion (*Matthew 5:7*)
7. giving something to others, allowing others to partake (*Ephesians 4:28*)
10. dependable (*1 Thessalonians 5:24*)
11. seeking the welfare of another (*John 13:34*)
12. a supervisory position in which one manages another's property (*Luke 12:42*)
13. a group of people who share life together (*Acts 4:32*)
14. willingly working with others (*1 Corinthians 16:16*)
15. self-regulation (*2 Peter 1:6*)
16. belief or trust (*2 Corinthians 5:7*)
20. a state of contentment, opposite of hostility (*Philippians 4:7*)
21. pardon (*Matthew 6:14*)

Fundamental Option

> *"I have set before you life and death . . ."*
>
> —Deuteronomy 30:19

Part A.

Directions: Read the following description of the concept of fundamental option.

Fundamental option is a theological concept that addresses the way in which we use our God-given freedom. Each of us can use the gift of free will either to choose to do God's will in our lives or to reject it and follow our own will. As our lives progress, we choose a basic direction that orients us either toward or away from God. We choose to be a particular kind of human being, either one who discovers his or her true self in God and thus reaches potential, or one who, like Adam and Eve, believes that he or she knows what is best.

This choice underlies all of our other choices. It influences our daily decisions. It is the choice of a direction of life or a way of living. It is related to the concept called inner freedom or free will, in which we are confronted with one basic choice—in our lives will we choose to do God's will or our own will? How we answer that question will affect all of the other significant and superficial choices we make. Fundamental option is the most basic choice of all. When we act consistently with our fundamental option, we deepen it; it becomes more fully ingrained in our lives and gives our daily activities a more profound meaning and unity. Acting contrary to it, we undermine its stability. Sin can be understood as acting in a way that says no to becoming the person God desires us to be. It is to choose a pattern of living that acts inconsistently with our option for God and distances us from God.

Our fundamental option is realized in the many individual choices we make throughout each day. The pattern that emerges in our daily lives gives evidence of our fundamental option. Pattern doesn't mean whether we get up in the morning or go to bed at night at the same time each day. Rather fundamental option means whether our lives reflect a pattern of loving God, neighbor, self, and the world in what we say and do and think, or not.

Keep this in mind: it is possible to commit mortal sin. Mortal sin is the degree of sin that destroys our relationship with God. It is possible, in a series of actions or in one dramatic action, to cut off oneself totally from the love of God. (See the *Catechism of the Catholic Church,* 1861.) Fundamental option means that we have an option. A definitive rejection of God's invitation to friendship is possible, through either a deadly series of sinful actions or in one grave mortal sin.

To summarize, fundamental option is the basic choice of a direction of living or way of life that says either yes or no to becoming the fullest possible person we can become in God. It is the acceptance or the rejection of the invitation to be a part of God's kingdom. It determines our ultimate destiny.

Kingdom of God vs. Kingdom of the World

Part B.

Directions: The following chart provides guideposts to evaluate our fundamental option.

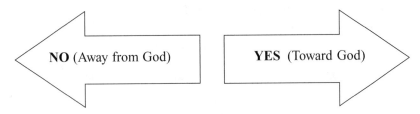

We choose	We choose
• Self	• God
• Our will	• God's will
• Selfishness	• Love
• The kingdom of the world	• The kingdom of God
• To be "getters"	• To be "givers"
• Things	• Relationships
• To stay with what is safe or familiar	• To risk in order to grow
• Hell	• Heaven

89

A Personal Inventory

Directions: List on the appropriate scale areas in your life that are evidence of the ways in which you are moving toward and away from God. Remember that our destiny is to be convicted of having tipped the scale definitively toward God, God's love, and doing good to others. Remember, too, that the choices you make will influence the direction your life will take in the future. Which way is your scale leaning?

Away from God   **Toward God**

People judge you by your actions, not by your intentions. You may have a heart of gold— but so does a hard boiled egg.

—Don Ameche

90

Afterlife Images

Part A.

Directions: The Catholic tradition identifies three possible forms of afterlife—heaven, hell, and purgatory. Draw a picture, an image, or a symbol that represents your understanding of each of these realities.

Heaven

Hell

In Hell they say Heaven is a great lie.

—Daniel Berrigan, S.J.

Purgatory

Part B.

Directions: Answer the following questions regarding afterlife.

1. What do you think happens after death?

2. What do you think judgment is? How will that judgment take place? Write a paragraph describing your judgment.

3. What is your idea of heaven? Will it be fun? Why or why not? Do you want to be there? Why or why not?

4. Give a description of your idea of hell.

5. What does purgatory mean to you?

6. Explain in as much detail as possible when, where, and how you came to these concepts of judgment—heaven, hell, and purgatory.

Why I Believe There Is Life after Death: A Parable

Directions: Read the following passage, and answer the questions.

Lord Thomson of Fleet was one of the great newspapermen of our era. At one time he owned some 240 publications in England, Scotland, Canada, and the United States.

One day, he invited me to a luncheon in the sumptuous dining room of the *London Times*. The table was made up of distinguished editors and writers as well as prominent businessmen. The conversation ranged over many themes: world affairs, politics British and American, the prospects for world peace. Suddenly, in the midst of much good-natured banter, Thomson said, "Dr. Peale, I am an old man, and one of these days I'm going to die." The room became silent. "I want to know: Is there an afterlife?"

I couldn't be sure he wasn't pulling my leg, but then I sensed that the question was indeed serious and weighed on his mind. "Lord Thomson," I said, "I believe in the promises in the Bible. But beyond the Biblical is the evidence of intelligence and common sense."

Then I told him and the others a parable about a prenatal baby tucked beneath his mother's loving heart. "Suppose," I said, "someone came to this unborn baby and said, 'You cannot stay here long. In a few months you will be born, or, as you may think of it, die out of your present state.'

"The baby might stubbornly say, 'I don't want to leave here. I'm warm, loved and happy. I don't want to be what you call born, or what I call die, out of this place.'

"But he is born. He does die out of his present life. And what does he find? He feels beneath him strong, loving arms. He looks up into a beautiful face, tender with love, the face of his mother. He is welcomed, cared for, and says, 'How foolish I was. This is a wonderful place to which I have come.'

"Then he goes on to enjoy the delights of childhood. He grows into youth with its excitement and romance. He marries, and knows the love of his children.

"The years pass, with the strength of manhood, the achievement of middle age; the joy and wonderment of life are his. Then he becomes an old man. His step slows.

> *Death is not a foe, but an inevitable adventure.*
>
> —Sir Oliver Lodge

93

Someone says, 'You are going to die, or, as we call it, be born out of this place into another.'

"And he might remonstrate: 'But I don't want to die. I have loved ones. I love this world—the dawn and sunset, the moon, the starlight. I like to feel the warmth of the fire on my face when cold weather comes, and to hear the crunch of snow beneath my feet on a winter's evening. I don't want to leave this world. I don't want to die.'

"But in natural course he does die. What happens then? Is God, the Creator, suddenly going to change His nature? Can we not assume that he will once again feel loving arms beneath him, and once again look up into a strong, beautiful face, more lovely even than that first face he saw so long ago?

"Won't he soon be exclaiming, 'Why, this is wonderful! Here I want to remain forever.'

"Does this not make sense?" I concluded. A deep silence hung over the table; several of the company appeared to be moved.

Thomson sighed. "It does indeed make sense," he said. "I will never forget that parable. It has helped me answer a question that has haunted me for years." Suddenly his mood changed. "Do you think I will like it over there?"

"Of course, for it will be exciting."

"What will I do there?" he asked with a grin.

"Perhaps buy and sell newspapers!" A laugh went around the luncheon table.

Since then, Lord Thomson has gone on into the life beyond. And, judging by the affirmative way this lovable man responded to the power of faith, I think God must be taking good care of him.[1]

1. Does the parable make sense to you? Explain why or why not.

[1]Adapted from *The Positive Power of Jesus Christ,* Norman Vincent Peale (Wheaton, Ill.: Tyndale House Publishers, 1980), 146–50.

2. How does the parable agree or conflict with your understanding of afterlife?

3. Does the idea of afterlife excite you?

4. C. S. Lewis says that the devil leads us to think about heaven the way we should think about hell. What do you believe he means in that statement?

A Theological Understanding of Afterlife

> *Fear not that your life shall come to an end, but rather fear that it shall never have a beginning.*
>
> —Cardinal Newman

Directions: People have believed in the existence of a spirit world and in life after death since ancient times. Evidence of this belief can be seen in the elaborate burial rituals in Egyptian tombs and in the burial customs of Native American peoples. Both of these cultures buried articles to be used in the next life along with the body. There has never been complete agreement about the existence of an afterlife or about the nature of that afterlife. Among the Jews of Jesus' day, the Sadducees did not believe in an afterlife; the Pharisees believed in a dwelling place of the dead called Sheol, but they were not sure of its nature. Jesus spoke of a continuing existence after death in terms of heaven and hell. The following scriptural passages give insight into the afterlife, as well as theological understandings of heaven, hell, and purgatory. Summarize the key concept for each scriptural passage.

Heaven

Matthew 5:8

Matthew 25:31–40

John 6:39

John 14:1–3

1 Corinthians 15:51–53

1 Corinthians 15:35–44

- Heaven is a state of being completely happy and loved.

- It is total union of the individual with God (the beatific vision).

- We will become fully like God, capable of perfect love, free of all selfishness.

- Life after death is communal. We will become a part of the communion of saints, linked to those who have lived before us in faith and to those who live after us on earth. That is why we, the living on earth, pray to the saints in heaven to intercede for us.

- In the resurrection of the body, we will be transformed.

Kingdom of God vs. Kingdom of the World

Hell

Mark 9:43–48

Matthew 10:28

Revelation 19:20

Matthew 8:12

Matthew 25:40–46

- The valley of Gehenna was the site of infant sacrifice when the Canaanites occupied the land prior to the Israelite conquest of the region. Because this practice was considered an abomination to God, this area outside of Jerusalem became the city's garbage dump. Refuse was constantly being burned there; consequently, the fires never went out. The reference is symbolic. Gehenna was associated with wickedness, a repulsive place and one to be avoided. Jesus' use of this reference places the emphasis on the never-ending nature of the experience rather than on the element of fire.

- Jesus did not preach fear of hell. Rather, he emphasized that if one did not choose the kingdom of God, hell was all that remained. He was not trying to describe a particular place.

- Hell is the absence of God. It is the choice of those who reject God, reject community with others, and choose an existence lacking any true meaning.

- Its nature is isolation and separation from the community of love. It is characterized by loneliness, unhappiness, and despair.

- God does not punish people by sending them to hell. Rather, because he respects our free will, he reluctantly yields to the choice we make when we reject God and others through our failure to love.

Purgatory

2 Maccabees 12:38–46

1 Corinthians 3:12–15

- There is no clear biblical reference to purgatory.

- Purgatory is a process or experience by which we are purged (cleansed) of our self-centeredness, which keeps us from full union with God. This purging is necessary because nothing selfish or un-loving can enter heaven, the perfection of love. We need to let go of anything that holds us back from completely giving ourselves in love to God.

- The fact that the individual is not fully with God causes him or her pain. It is the pain of regret, knowing that we settled for less than God desired for us. We did not accept the love he offered us.

- It is a painful experience as we surrender our will to God so that he might complete the work of transforming us into his image.

- Prayers and sacrifices may be offered by the living on earth for those who have died that they may be soon healed of any residual selfishness and can surrender completely to God.

"The Return"—Beverly Steigerwald

Part 6

Personal Conversion

What do you mean by "born again"? I thought that was something only Protestants (and Nicodemus) did!

Each of us is called individually and personally to follow Jesus Christ as a disciple. Answering that call is a lifelong process.

Do I Value Jesus?

Part A.

Directions: Reflect on your Christian faith and values as you read the following information.

Dr. Sidney B. Simon, an authority on values, says that there are seven conditions that must be met if something is to be a value. If even one of these conditions is not met, it cannot be considered a value. It may be a goal or an ideal, but it is not a value.

A value is . . .

- prized and cherished
- publicly affirmed, when appropriate
- chosen from alternatives
- chosen after consideration of consequences
- freely chosen
- acted upon
- acted upon with a pattern, consistency, and repetition[1]

Part B.

Directions: Answer the following reflection questions. Contemplate whether your Christian faith would meet the conditions in part A to be called a value in your life.

1. Have you ever personally chosen to follow Jesus in your life, or is this simply a decision that your parents made for you when you were young?

2. Have you ever given thought to other ways of living out your life, either in terms of another religious tradition or simply through choosing to live your life following your own will rather than God's will?

The Christian ideal has not been tried and found wanting. It has been found difficult, and left untried.

—G. K. Chesterton

101

[1]Adapted from *Values Clarification,* Sidney B. Simon, et al. (New York: Warner Books, 1995), 19.

3. Are you aware of what is expected of you in terms of attitudes, lifestyle, and values if you say you are a Christian?

4. How important is your faith to you? Which has greater influence in your life—your faith or your peers? Would you be willing to sacrifice or die for your faith as the martyrs did?

5. Can others see evidence of your Christian faith in the way you live your life? As the old question asks, "If Christians were put on trial, would there be enough evidence to convict you?"

6. Is your faith something that you practice? Is it more than just an attitude of belief in God? Is your faith something that affects your decision making and the way you live your life?

7. Have you developed patterns or practices to live out your Christian faith? Is your faith something you turn to only in times of need or crisis? Is your faith commitment something that is lived on a daily basis rather than just something you do at Mass on Sunday?

Part C.

Directions: After honestly and thoughtfully reflecting on the questions in part B, write an essay explaining how your Christian faith either is or is not a value in your life.

Are You Saved?

Part A.

Directions: Read and reflect on the following explanation of fundamentalist and Catholic views of conversion.

Have you ever been asked, "Are you saved?" by a friend or acquaintance? Has someone you know claimed to have been "born again"? Has a zealous Christian ever told you that you have to "accept Jesus as your personal savior"? Many Catholics have had such experiences and have found themselves confused by these unfamiliar phrases. Yet these concepts do have their origin in Scripture. Let us examine passages from which these terms are derived.

> [F]or, if you confess with your mouth that
> Jesus is Lord and believe in your heart that
> God raised him from the dead, you will be
> saved.
>
> —*Romans 10:9*

Fundamentalist and evangelical Christians maintain that if a person has accepted Jesus as Lord and Savior, then salvation is assured. Their belief is that by following this scriptural formula, a person comes into a personal relationship with Jesus; as this relationship is lived out, one ultimately experiences salvation. Christians who believe in this model of spirituality say that their Christian faith is not just an intellectual belief. It is an experiential reality. They experience the saving power of God in their day-to-day lives.

The central belief statement of Christianity is that Jesus is Lord and Savior. This belief distinguishes Christians from all other religious traditions. However, while we use these terms frequently, we may not understand what they mean. *Lord* refers to one who is in charge, a master or ruler. When we say Jesus is our Lord, we are saying that we have chosen to surrender our wills to the will of Jesus, and we will seek his direction for our lives. No longer is Jesus just one of many realities in our lives; he becomes the center of our lives, and he directs how we live.

When we consider Jesus' role as Savior, we mean that he saves us from our sins. But what does that mean? We believe that his death and resurrection free us from the power of sin. He helps us when we are unable to help ourselves. The testimony of many people who use the Twelve-Step model of spirituality developed by Alcoholics Anonymous and adopted by other recovery groups is that when they turned their will and their lives over to God, God was able to do for them what they could not do for themselves. Accepting Jesus as one's personal Lord and Savior is an acceptance of God's gift of salvation.

103

Born-again Christians take their name from a passage in John's Gospel.

> Now there was a Pharisee named Nicodemus, a ruler of the Jews. He came to Jesus at night and said to him, "Rabbi we know that you are a teacher who has come from God, for no one can do these signs that you are doing unless God is with him." Jesus answered and said to him, "Amen, amen, I say to you, no one can see the kingdom of God without being born from above." Nicodemus said to him, "How can a person once grown old be born again? Surely he cannot reenter his mother's womb and be born again, can he?" Jesus answered, "Amen, amen I say to you, no one can enter the kingdom of God without being born of water and Spirit."
> —*John 3:1–5*

Christians claiming to have had a born-again experience maintain that water baptism is not sufficient in itself. There must be spiritual rebirth as well. This occurs when they personally commit themselves to follow Jesus and ask that the gift and power of the Holy Spirit be released in their lives. God respects our free will and will not force us to conversion. God offers us gifts and waits until we give permission to pour out the Spirit upon us. Many people who have had a born-again experience say that once they invited Jesus to take charge of their lives, they had a personal and experiential encounter with God. It is often a profound experience of unconditional love. They relate that this experience is so significant and so changes their basic beliefs about what is important that it is as though their lives began anew from that moment.

While fundamentalist and evangelical Christians see this as a one-time experience, the Catholic Christian tradition understands initial conversion in broader terms. Rather than emphasizing a particular, dramatic occasion when one makes this choice, the Catholic tradition stresses a process that may occur over a period of time. It starts with the Sacrament of Baptism, usually received at infancy, in which God's grace washes sin from us, including original sin, recreates us as adopted children of God and members of Christ's Body, the Church, and fills us with the Holy Spirit. It may be a series of small yeses to the Lord, allowing God to enter more deeply into our lives. It may be a gradual growth in awareness of the place and importance of God in our lives or a new seriousness in our resolve to follow Jesus. It includes the Sacrament of Confirmation, in which the local bishop confirms our full membership in the church, resealing us with the Holy Spirit, and we have the opportunity to speak for ourselves to renew our baptismal promises and affirm our personal relationship with Jesus Christ.

Whichever tradition we follow, evangelical or Catholic, the choice of yielding to Jesus in our lives must someday become conscious, something to which we are committed, if we are serious in our desire to grow in holiness and to experience the fullness of salvation.

Part B.

Directions: Write a thoughtful essay in which you answer the following questions.

1. If you had to do it all over again, would you get baptized? Why or why not? (If you have never been baptized, explain why not.)

2. If you had to do it all over again, would you receive the Sacrament of Confirmation? Why or why not? (If you have never been confirmed, explain why not.)

Exercise 50

Willing Spirit/Weak Flesh

Directions: Each player rolls a die. The person with the highest number starts, and play proceeds clockwise. A player must roll a one to start. When players land on a blank space, their turn ends. On the other blocks, the player must follow the directions. Players can enter into God's kingdom only on an exact roll of the die. The first person to enter into the kingdom is the winner.

	You choose not to commit your life to Jesus because of your fear that he will ask you to give up something you like. Go back one space.	You disagree with and ignore the Church's teaching on pre-marital sex. Go back two spaces.	

After getting drunk and in trouble with your parents again, you go to Confession and decide to stop drinking. Go ahead one space.		At your senior retreat you tell Jesus sincerely that you want to grow close to him. Jump ahead three spaces.	

106

You did not study for a test and just prayed for God to help you. Lose one turn.			You take the Confirmation preparation program seriously. Roll again.

	You are asked to be a lector at Mass because of your good example. Advance one space.		You pray for a new bike, but you do not get it for your birthday. You begin to doubt God. Go back one space.

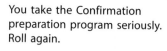

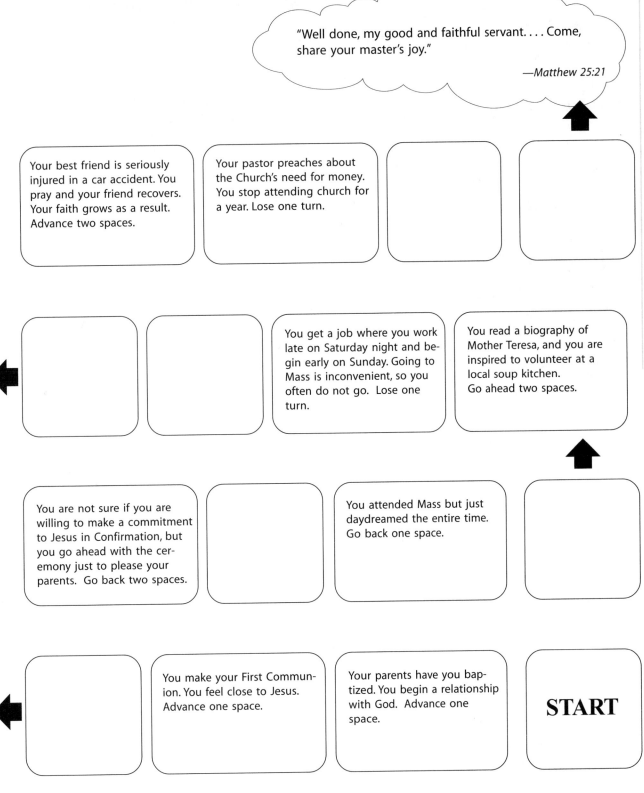

"Well done, my good and faithful servant. . . . Come, share your master's joy."

—Matthew 25:21

Your best friend is seriously injured in a car accident. You pray and your friend recovers. Your faith grows as a result. Advance two spaces.

Your pastor preaches about the Church's need for money. You stop attending church for a year. Lose one turn.

You get a job where you work late on Saturday night and begin early on Sunday. Going to Mass is inconvenient, so you often do not go. Lose one turn.

You read a biography of Mother Teresa, and you are inspired to volunteer at a local soup kitchen. Go ahead two spaces.

You are not sure if you are willing to make a commitment to Jesus in Confirmation, but you go ahead with the ceremony just to please your parents. Go back two spaces.

You attended Mass but just daydreamed the entire time. Go back one space.

You make your First Communion. You feel close to Jesus. Advance one space.

Your parents have you baptized. You begin a relationship with God. Advance one space.

START

Personal Conversion

A Historical Overview of the Sacrament of Reconciliation

> The final word is not that we have sinned, but that we have been forgiven.
>
> —Daniel Berrigan, S.J.

108

Directions: Read the following summary of the history of the Church's Sacrament of Reconciliation.

During the course of the Church's history, the Sacrament of Reconciliation has taken on different forms of celebration. Based on the need for reconciliation, the Church, through its various stages of growth and development devised rites in keeping with its understanding of sin. A brief historical scheme is given below. The scriptural roots of the sacrament emerge from the account of Jesus' appearance to the Apostles on Easter Sunday night. Jesus greeted the frightened Apostles with the words, "Peace be with you" (*John 20:19*). Then he commissioned them to be ministers of that same peace: "As the Father has sent me, so I send you" (*John 20:21*). He breathed on them and said, "Receive the holy Spirit. Whose sins you forgive are forgiven them, and whose sins you retain are retained" (*John 20:22–23*).

Jesus' ministry to sinners was recognized and emphasized by the Evangelists. Through the Gospels, we read of Jesus' constant association with sinners and tax collectors. His proclamation that the kingdom of God was at hand was accompanied by a statement of his basic mission: "Those who are well do not need a physician, but the sick do. I did not come to call the righteous but sinners" (*Mark 2:17*). Throughout the Gospels, we hear him speak the words, "Your sins are forgiven," in response to people's faith. Jesus' commission to the Apostles continued a central aspect of his ministry, the work of reconciliation.

In the early Church, conversion usually involved adults who saw Jesus' call as the catalyst for transformed lives. The ritual of Baptism celebrated freedom from their former sinful lives. Thus in Baptism an individual's sins were all forgiven. Baptized Christians were expected to live exemplary virtuous lives. To aid the believers, the practice of Liturgical Penance evolved. At the liturgy, Christians confessed their sins to one another in the context of a community who forgave them, supported them in their growth in holiness, prayed for them, and admonished and corrected them when necessary. We retain this early tradition in the penitential rite at the beginning of the Mass.

During the second century, concern arose about those who, despite their baptismal release from sin, fell into serious sins, such as murder, adultery, or apostasy (giving up one's faith under pressure during periods of persecution). A new practice developed. Failure to live a life consistent with the call to holiness called for penance. In the case of serious sins, ecclesial penance was limited to one reception during a person's lifetime. This practice, which continued until the sixth century, involved a new form of the Sacrament of Penance, public penance.

Liturgical Penance was still available for minor sins, but for serious sins, an individual had to go before the bishop and the community. In order to be readmitted into the local community, the sinner was enrolled in the Order of Penitents and assigned public penance. Since the sins were a matter of public knowledge, atonement also had to be a public expression of contrition. The penance included a visible sign of repentance through the donning of sackcloth and ashes (a practice which usually denoted that one was in mourning). Partial exclusion from the community meant that the sinner was required to leave the celebration of the Eucharist prior to the Offertory. A specific penance, usually rigorous, was imposed by the bishop. The Church also provided prayerful support, and eventual restoration to the community was represented by the bishop's imposition of hands at the completion of one's period of penance. Those guilty of less serious sins often were given penances of specific prayers, fasting, and acts of charity. After the rite of public penance disappeared, these elements evolved into our liturgical season of Lent.

During the sixth century, the Irish monks brought about major change in the sacrament. They recognized that the practice of forgiveness only once for serious sins was inconsistent with Jesus' revelation of a loving Father and with his admonition to Peter that one must forgive whenever the occasion calls for forgiveness. The monks developed the practice of private penance. Forgiveness became a matter between the priest and penitent. Repeated penance and reconciliation became the norm. Now the priest represented the community and continued its ministry of forgiving sin and nurturing virtue as the community had done in earlier eras.

During the Middle Ages, a significant change was made: reconciliation took place immediately after confession of sins. Attention shifted from the penance to the absolution spoken by the priest. The confessing of one's sins, the laying open of one's guilt and shame, was seen as the sign of penitent's conversion of heart. The sacrament came under much criticism during the Protestant Reformation. Many Reformation churches discontinued its use. In response, the Council of Trent reaffirmed its values and set the conditions for its receptions: confession, contrition and satisfaction by the penitent, absolution from the priest. The practice of anonymous confession in a confessional box emerged. In the first half of the twentieth century, frequent confession was the norm. Devout Catholics would go to confession weekly; priests would spend hours on the weekend in the confessional box hearing confessions.

Like all the other sacraments, this sacrament was revised by the Second Vatican Council. Three rites for celebrating the sacrament were approved: traditional individual confession with a brief celebration of

God's word of forgiveness; a longer communal penance service with time for individual confession, and a communal service with general absolution (which may only be used in emergency circumstance). Today the Sacrament of Reconciliation emphasizes healing, reconciliation with God, self, and others, and one's personal encounter with a loving Christ. The style of confessing is more personal. One's state of being, including practices which harm us and others or which prevent us from loving ourselves, is more important than a "grocery list" recitation of sins.

An Examination of Conscience

Directions: When asked which is the greatest commandment, Jesus replied, "The first is this: 'Hear, O Israel! The Lord our God is Lord alone! You shall love the Lord your God with all your heart, with all your soul, with all your mind, and with all your strength.' The second is this: 'You shall love your neighbor as yourself'" (*Mark 12:29–31*). Christians understand sin as a failure to live in accordance with this commandment. All Christians need to take the opportunity on a regular basis to examine their conscience and behavior towards others. The following questions are presented to aid you in taking personal inventory.

"You shall love the Lord your God with all your heart."

1. Do I really love God before all things? Are there things of this world I put before him—money, possessions, pleasure, popularity, acceptance, desires, ambitions, or any other limited things?

2. Do I recognize and acknowledge God's authority over my life? Do I choose my will over God's will?

3. Do I spend time growing in love for God? Do I only go before him when it is convenient or I am in need? Do I pray to him daily? Do I participate each Sunday in the celebration of the Eucharist?

4. Do I love and revere God's name?

5. Have I participated in the occult through fortune-telling, astrology, palm reading or other superstitious activities where I seek direction for my life from someone other than God?

"Love your neighbor"

1. What is the quality of my love for others? Am I respectful of people in authority over me? Do I honor my parents by showing them respect and obedience? How do I relate to my teachers and my employer? Do I act in a loving manner toward my siblings, friends, and coworkers?

2. Have I lost control of my temper and my speech? Do I exercise self-discipline?

3. Do I finish my responsibilities and do my best in my work?

4. Do I hold grudges or resentments? Is there anyone I have not forgiven?

5. Have I said things that have hurt others or done damage to their reputation, honor, or dignity?

6. Am I honest in my dealings with others? Am I fair toward other people? Do I judge unfairly?

7. Have I stolen from others or failed to make restitution when I have done so?

> *Labor to keep alive in your heart that little spark of celestial fire called conscience.*
>
> —George Washington

111

8. Do I take time to consider the consequences of my actions on others?

9. Do I allow myself to be prejudiced or treat others in a discriminatory manner?

10. Do I take my frustrations or moods out on others, particularly those closest to me?

11. Do I share my possessions and talents with others who are less fortunate? Am I self-centered? Do I do my best to help the victims of oppression, misfortune, and poverty?

12. Have I done violence to others or their property?

13. Have I manipulated or used others for my own selfish purposes?

14. Have I given myself over to lustful thoughts or actions? Do I use obscene or off-color language or tell inappropriate stories? Do I indulge in pornography or unsuitable movies or television programs? Have I used others for my own sexual satisfaction or exposed them to risk? Am I modest in the way I dress?

15. Am I envious of others' possessions or looks?

16. Have I driven in a way that could put others at risk?

17. Do I act in a manner that gives a good example to others? Am I a good witness to my faith?

"As yourself"

1. Do I thank God for the blessings in my life and use the capabilities and talents he has given me? What uses have I made of my time, health, and strength?

2. Have I been responsible in my driving, eating, drinking, and smoking habits? Have I abused my body through the misuse of drugs or alcohol? Have I put myself at risk through my sexual behavior? Do I have a wholesome attitude toward my sexuality?

3. Can I forgive myself when I make mistakes or fail to live up to my standards?

4. Have I accepted the sorrows and disappointments in life without closing myself off?

5. Do I make appropriate use of my educational opportunities to grow and develop my skills?

6. Do I try to keep a cheerful and positive disposition? Do I give in to self-pity and depression? Do I let fears limit my potential freedom?

7. Do I seek counseling, spiritual direction, and other aids to my personal growth?

"A Warm Embrace"—Timothy P. Schmalz

Part 7

Growing in Relationship with Jesus

Our faith in God can grow. We can nurture our faith development and help it mature through a variety of techniques. Some are suggested by the exercises in this unit.

Imagination and Sacred Story

Directions: Story can have a powerful effect on our lives. Listening to the stories of others helps us to understand them and grow in relationship with them. Telling our own stories tells others who we are and what we are about. God, too, speaks to us through the stores of Scripture. To pray well, we need to read and meditate on the pages of Scripture frequently. Complete the following exercise. Use your imagination! Note your responses after each question.

1. Read *1 Corinthians 13.*

    a. Which phrase(s) strike you as particularly meaningful? Why?

    b. What do you think the main lesson of this passage is?

    c. Now read the passage again, but this time replace the word *love* with your name every time it comes up in the text. Which phrase(s) now strike you as particularly meaningful? Why?

    d. What is different about reading the passage this way?

    e. What insights, ideas, or feelings does the passage evoke?

Change the name and it's about you, that story.

—Horace

115

2. Read *John 18:15–18* and *25–27*.

   a. Try to imagine yourself watching the scene as it takes place. Have you ever been betrayed by a friend? What emotions does the scene evoke in you?

   b. What insights does the passage give you about the nature of the friendship between Peter and Jesus?

   c. Now reread the passage. This time imagine that Jesus is walking past Peter as the cock crows and the two exchange glances. Describe the look Jesus gives to Peter.

   d. What does this reveal about the nature of the friendship between Jesus and Peter?

   e. How might this insight apply to the nature of your own friendships with others? with someone who has betrayed you?

3. How was the experience of Scripture changed by personalizing the reading, that is, by putting a little of yourself and your imagination into the reading?

116

Where to Look

Directions: Scripture can answer many of life's questions and help us to deal with the problems we face. Read the quotation about Scripture. Then follow the Scripture meditation process to pray one of the passages listed below. Answer the questions at the end of the exercise.

> All scripture is inspired by God and is useful for teaching, for refutation, for correction, and for training in righteousness, so that one who belongs to God may be competent, equipped for every good work.
>
> *—2 Timothy 3:16*

Feeling guilty?	Pray *Psalm 51:3–21.*
Tired?	Pray *Psalm 23:1–6.*
Feeling hassled?	Pray *Isaiah 26:4–13.*
Need to make a decision?	Pray *Proverbs 3:1–12.*
Need courage?	Pray *Ephesians 6:10–17.*
Afraid?	Pray *Psalm 27:1–6.*
Happy?	Pray *Psalm 96:1–12.*
Said something wrong?	Pray *James 3:1–11.*
Feeling left out?	Pray *Luke 6:17–49.*
Feeling unqualified?	Pray *Jeremiah 1:4–10.*
Feeling alone and unloved?	Pray *Isaiah 43:1–8.*
Hate following rules?	Pray *Romans 13:1–7.*
Want to be a good friend?	Pray *Sirach 6:5–17.*
Mourning the death of a loved one?	Pray *Wisdom 3:1–12.*

1. Is there any word or phrase in the passage that particularly struck you?

2. What were your feelings as you prayed the passage? Were you peaceful, loving, trusting, angry, sad, discouraged? What do these feelings say to you?

3. What insights have you gained into yourself after praying this passage?

One of the five things about prayer is that it shuts out the noise of the world.

—Dwight D. Eisenhower

117

Prayer

Directions: Read the following article about the meaning and importance of prayer. Then answer the questions.

Prayer is a journey inward. It is a journey into our hearts. Just as the heart is the "life-giving pulsation" of our physical make-up, so prayer is the "life-giving pulsation" that gives meaning to our lives. It gives meaning to our lives because it is a journey inward into the HEART OF OURSELF in which we meet the HEART OF GOD. We journey inward to seek the mystery of a God who created us and lives within us—a God in whom "we live and move and have our being" (*Acts 17:28*). Prayer is a journey inward to touch this God of mystery.

And as we journey inward to the center of our person, searching for the relationship in which we touch the mystery of God, we touch the core of our being. For in seeking God, we seek ourselves, and in touching God, we touch ourselves. Creation takes on new meaning as the Creator takes on new meaning for us. God becomes alive in a new way as gradually, in experiencing him, a new sensitivity emerges within us. Through prayer, we become sensitive to the gentle touch of God in our lives. There is a new awareness of ourselves, of relationships, of the world, of the whole of creation because we are awakened to the Creator Who is love. We begin to SEE in a different way, and we begin to FEEL in a different way as a new sense of God penetrates our awareness—the love of God which is the foundation and the root of all life.

Prayer is like the BIRTH OF LOVE in our hearts. When we seek communication with the Lord on a regular prayer basis, then LITTLE MIRACLES OF LOVE seem to burst forth everywhere. Perhaps they happened before, but we were unaware of them. A rainbow colors the sky, and we are suddenly reminded of a Father-God and his care. We rejoice at beauty, and we rejoice in creation. We rejoice in the mystery of ourselves, in the fact that we are capable of experiencing this beauty. An azalea flashes its blossom, heralding the first promise of spring, and we gasp at its wonder, and we gasp at its Maker. The eyes of a friend shine brighter, and we feel a warmer handclasp. Laughter bubbles forth with a joyful spontaneity and pain wells forth with a new frequency as our sensitivity for others is heightened. As we bring ourselves before the Lord in fidelity of his trust and his care for us, there seems to be a freshness of life everywhere because when one begins to

More things are wrought by prayer than this world dreams of.

—Alfred, Lord Tennyson

118

touch the HEART OF GOD in prayer each day, then one begins to touch the HEART OF LIFE.

The journey of prayer is a life-long venture. It is a journey in which we become familiar with the way only when it is traveled regularly. At first, our day's journey may be short and then, little by little, we are able to travel longer as we become accustomed to the road which leads us inward. Companions may be needed—thoughts from others, Scripture helps, aids to guide us. The journey will take us to mountain tops as well as deep valleys. We will travel in the sunlight and we will travel in the night. At times, the touch of God will awe us with wonder; at times, lack of feeling will cause us to grope in anguish. Our journey is a mystery—a very personal mystery, however, because it is a journey into the mystery of a Person. Prayer is opening ourselves to the mystery of the Person of God within us, letting [the Spirit of God] activate our lives to the fullest.

Just as our relationship with a person deepens when we spend time in getting to know that person, so our relationship with God deepens when we spend time getting to know Him. Opening ourselves to [God] in surrender, we let [God] grace us with His presence, and He becomes a FRIEND-GOD. A friend is one with whom we can share our low moments as well as our high moments, our laughter as well as our tears. A friend will climb the mountains with us and go down into the valleys with us. A friend is always there for us. Sometimes, words are not necessary; presence only suffices. So it is with God and prayer. [God] is always there beckoning us into His presence, asking only for our openness to seek Him in faith, for He truly wants to be our FRIEND-GOD.[1]

1. "Prayer is a journey." This idea implies that prayer is a continual and growing awareness of another rather than an activity to be completed once. Is this concept similar to or different from your current understanding of prayer? Explain.

[1]Lou Collison, *Abba, Father: Prayer Journal* (Phoenix: North American Liturgy Resources, 1979), 7.

2. The author states that prayer is the "life-giving pulsation that gives meaning to our lives." Does prayer currently fill this role in your life? Explain.

3. Paragraph two implies that prayer changes us more than it changes God. What does this imply about what we pray for?

4. Prayer is essentially our primary means of communication with God. Communication is a two-way street. Both parties must be willing to share of themselves in order for true communication to exist. What do you typically share with God? What does God typically share with you? Do you see room for improvement in your communication with God?

5. The article explains that "little miracles of love" are the product of regular prayer. Describe an incident in which you were reminded of God's love for you. How was prayer a part of this experience?

6. What things, people, and experiences help you to pray? Have you ever felt that your prayers were unheard or unanswered? Explain. How do you cope with those feelings?

7. The author describes our relationship to God in terms of friendship. Is this how you experience God? What other images might also describe your relationship to God right now?

8. The last paragraph refers to the fact that sometimes words are not necessary—simply feeling the presence of God is sufficient for prayer. Describe when you have felt God's presence in your life most clearly.

Praying with the People of God

Directions: Scripture is full of outstanding examples of people who prayed. Abraham, Moses, David, and Solomon are Old Testament examples. In the New Testament, Jesus prayed, and so impressed his disciples that they asked him to teach them how to pray. As you look up each passage and answer the questions, think about what you can learn about prayer from the example of the biblical people of faith and from the teaching of Jesus.

1. *Genesis 18:22–32*—What does Abraham's bargaining prayer reveal about his faith in God?

2. *Exodus 3:1–10*—How is this scene a striking example of prayer?

3. *Exodus 17:1–7*—What is the role of Moses' prayer in this story?

4. *2 Samuel 7:18–29*—Why was King David considered a model of prayer?

5. *1 Kings 8:27–30*—What does Solomon's prayer at the dedication of the temple suggest about the temple's role in Israel's prayer life?

> "My soul proclaims the greatness of the Lord . . ."
>
> —Luke 1:46

6. *Luke 11:1–4*—How are the disciples to pray? What do you think is the most important line in the Lord's Prayer?

7. *Luke 11:9–13*—Does God always hear our prayer? Why or why not?

8. *Luke 22:39–46*—Does prayer always get positive results? Why or why not?

9. *John 17:1–26*—List any three themes in Jesus' prayer that are needed in today's world.

10. *1 Thessalonians 5:16–18*—When is a good time to pray, and how often?

Prayer Inventory

Directions: Prayer is our communication link with God. Traditionally, prayer takes one of four forms: adoration, contrition, supplication, and thanksgiving. Each form reflects a different reason why we pray or what we are trying to say to God. Prayer can also follow different methods, such as spontaneous prayer, vocal prayer, meditation, and contemplation. A key to unlock prayer is to let God speak to us. How often do you pray? How varied is your prayer style? Answer the following questions about prayer in your life.

1. Think back over your last four prayer times. Approximately how much time (in minutes) did you spend in total?

   a. Of that total time, how much time did you spend adoring and praising God?

   b. Of that total time, how much time did you spend expressing sorrow for misdeeds?

   c. Of that total time, how much time did you spend thanking God for the blessings you received?

   d. Of that total time, how much time did you spend asking God for things?

   e. Of that total time, how much time did you spend silently listening to God?

2. Circle the types of prayer you feel comfortable doing.

vocal	in your room
silent	in school
using your own words	contemplation
formal (memorized) prayers	meditation
private	symbolic gesture
communal	fasting
in Church	retreat
outside	guided meditation (creative visualization)

3. Using the same list, write an "X" next to the types of prayer you have never tried.

4. Using the same list, write a "?" next to the types of prayer you would like to try.

Little Boy kneels at the foot of the bed, Droops on the little hand little gold head. Hush! Hush! Whisper who dares! Christopher Robin is saying his prayers.

—A. A. Milne

124

Broadening Your Perspective

Part A.

Directions: A healthy, adult prayer life includes a balance of prayer forms and methods. Compare four original prayers: one of adoration, one of contrition, one of thanksgiving, and one of supplication.

Part B.

Directions: Answer the following questions.

1. What do you consider to be the elements of quality prayer time?

2. If you could create the ideal environment for prayer, what would that be?

3. Suggest several ways to make formal prayers a more meaningful and fulfilling method of praying.

4. How are prayer and trust connected to each other? What can detract from the trust necessary in prayer?

5. When are the most appropriate times for individual prayer? for communal prayer? for spontaneous prayer? for formal prayer?

Part C.

Find out what each of the following prayer forms involves. Then choose one and write a research report on the method of prayer, its purpose, and the type of person attracted to it.

meditation	mysticism
contemplation	Liturgy of the Hours
poustinia	Ignatian Exercises
symbolic gesture	

The Seven Sacraments

Part A.

Directions: Sacraments relate believers to the Church and to Christ, who is encountered in the Sacraments. They are signs of the unseen reality that is believed by those who participate ritually. They are signs of Christ's presence and especially of the mystery of his death and resurrection. Through the sacraments, we grow in the new life of the Spirit. Complete the following statements about the sacraments.

1. The Sacraments of Initiation are

    a.

    b.

    c.

    They are called Sacraments of Initiation because

2. The Sacraments of Healing are

    a.

    b.

    They are called Sacraments of Healing because

3. The Sacraments of Vocation are

    a.

    b.

    They are called Sacraments of Vocation because

Part B.

Directions: Answer the following questions.

1. We are baptized and confirmed into a eucharistic community. What evidence is present in the Church today that gives witness to the centrality of Eucharist?

2. The Sacraments of Initiation celebrate our incorporation into the Christian process of life. Such a process demands continual conversion and healing. What are the areas in your own life that need conversion and healing? in your family? in your country? in your Church?

3. All Christians are called to the vocation of following the call of Christ. This call can be lived out in a variety of lifestyle choices: single, married, vowed religious, ordained deacon or priest. To which lifestyle are you attracted? Why? Have you examined other lifestyle choices? If not, why not?

Eucharist Is Community

Directions: Catholics believe that Christ is really present in the Sacrament of the Eucharist. Christ makes his Paschal Mystery present to us, feeds us with his body, and binds us together as a faith community. When we speak of the Body of Christ, we refer to the Risen Body, the body transformed and made glorious, the Body that unites the faithful in heaven and on earth. Read the designated passages and use the following questions to reflect on the Eucharist in your life and in the Church.

We come together as one community to share in the one bread and one cup. Read 1 *Corinthians 10:16–17*.

1. What are the signs of unity in the Church?

2. What are the signs of disunity in the Church?

3. In what ways can Eucharist be a source of healing for the division in our community?

We come to listen to the Word of God proclaimed in the Scripture. Read *John 1:14*.

4. How has the Word of God become flesh in your life?

5. The Liturgy of the Word becomes enfleshed in the Liturgy of the Eucharist. How does Eucharist challenge you to live the Gospel message of faith and hope?

We come to share the bread and wine. Read *John 6:32–40*.

6.   For what do you hunger?

7.   In what ways does Jesus Christ fill your hunger?

We come to share that we might become the Body of Christ. Read *John 6:41–59*.

8.   Christ's body was broken. In what ways are you broken?

9.   Christ's blood was poured out. His life was one of self-emptying love. In what ways do you "pour out your energies" for those you love?

10.   How are you the presence of Christ for other people?

Scriptural Communities

Directions: In the writings of St. Paul, the term *Body of Christ* is used to express the strength and importance of the relationship between Jesus Christ and those who belong to him. The term also has implications regarding the relationship Christians are to have with one another. As Christians, we are united to Christ and share in the power of the resurrection. Read the designated scriptural passages, and respond to the questions.

1. Read *Acts 2:42–47* and *Acts 4:32–37*. How would you describe the ideal Christian life as it was lived by the early Church community?

We live in a world that has narrowed into a neighborhood before it has broadened into a brotherhood.

—Lyndon B. Johnson

130

2. Read *Romans 12, Galatians 6:1–10, Philippians 2:1–18,* and *Colossians 3:5–17*. What, aside from belief in Christ, makes a community "Christian"?

Eucharistic Community

Directions: Read the following reflections on the Eucharist.

1. Our community of origin is that of a family. Jesus, too, was born into a family. The Gospel of Luke shows that from the moment of Jesus' birth, he nourished us in our relationship with God. Jesus was placed in a manger, a food trough, symbolizing the fact that God offers himself as nourishment for our world.

2. In the Emmaus story of Luke's Gospel, we learn of the disciples who recognized Christ's presence among them in the breaking of the bread. Today, we, too, recognize the presence of Christ in the breaking of the bread at Eucharist.

3. The synoptic Gospels all place the institution of Eucharist at the Last Supper. John's Gospel replaces this institution with the washing of the Apostles' feet. As a result, Eucharist and service are linked to one another. The eucharistic Christian community is called to radical transformation. We are called to announce to the world the possibilities open to all. Eucharist enables us to make manifest the ideals of community through service, cooperation, simplicity, prayer, joy, forgiveness, and love without limit. Only then are we able to enjoy true intimacy with God.

Give us this day our daily bread, and forgive us . . .

—Matthew 6:11-12a (KJV)

131

What Is Just?

Directions: The theme of justice runs throughout the Bible. Eliminating injustices and making the world more just for all are part of the call of God to put our faith into practice by loving our neighbor. Read the following passages and determine the central truth of each.

1.   *Sirach 4:1–10*

2.   *Isaiah 58:2–14*

3.   *Amos 5:7–17*

4.   *Matthew 25:31–46*

5.   *Mark 12:41–44*

One trouble with the world is that so many people who stand up vigorously for their rights fall down miserably on their duties.

132

6. *Luke 10:25–37*

7. *John 13:1–17*

8. *2 Corinthians 8:8–15*

9. *1 Thessalonians 5:12–22*

10. *1 John 4:19–21*

Designing a Service Project

I am only one, but still I am one. I cannot do everything, but still I can do something; And because I cannot do everything I will not refuse to do the something that I can do.

—Edward Everett Hale

Directions: Follow the steps for designing a service project. Your teacher will assign a project deadline.

1. Choose your area of concern.

   The world is full of problems. Pick one that you would like to address. To help you choose an area, ask yourself these questions.

   - What do I personally value in life? Is there any area where these values are violated in the lives of others?

   - What talents, skills, and personality characteristics do I possess? Can I use these assets in my service project?

   - What opportunities are available to me in this area? Can I offer my services to already established projects such as soup kitchens and letter-writing campaigns?

   - What am I uncomfortable doing? What kind of a project am I not skilled to do? What concerns do my parents have about my duties?

   - Realistically, what type of commitment can I give in view of my other responsibilities?

2. Research what you can do.

   - Investigate how to volunteer for an already existing program, or decide to try something different. If you need some ideas, then the following list of books may help.

   Council on Economic Priorities. *Shopping for a Better World*. New York: Ballantine, 1992.

   Cowan, Ari. *50 Ways to Stop the Violence Now*. London: W. W. Norton & Company, 1996.

   Earth Works Group. *50 Simple Things You Can Do to Save the Earth*. New York: G. K. Hall, 1991.

   Hollender, John. *How to Make the World a Better Place: 116 Ways You Can Make A Difference*. London: W. W. Norton & Company, 1995.

   Kenyon, Thomas, and Justine Blau. *What You Can Do to Help the Homeless*. New York: Simon & Schuster, 1991.

   Lovell, V. ed. *AIDS in Africa: Help the Victims or Ignore Them*. Hauppauge, N.Y.: Nova Science Publishers, 2002.

   Nisbet, E. G. *Leaving Eden: To Protect and Manage the Earth*. Cambridge: Cambridge University Press, 2002.

   Sjogren, Steve and Janie. *101 Ways to Help People in Need*. Colorado Springs, Colo.: Navpress, 2002.

134

3. Plan a project. Do something!

   Determine the following:
   - *Whom* you will help
   - *What* you will do
   - *When* you will do this
   - *Where* you will work
   - *Why* you want to do this and not something else

4. Inform your teacher of your choice, and get approval for the project.

> *You will always have happiness if you seek and find how to serve.*
>
> —Dr. Albert Schweitzer

136

Service Project Worksheet

Directions: To aid your teacher in evaluating the effectiveness of your project, write a report on your activity.

Your report should include the following things:

- a description of your project, including specific details about whom you served and where the project took place

- research about your project, including political, social, and religious roots of the problem, as well as information about relevant service agencies

- a description of your feelings about what you experienced, including a summary of what you learned about yourself and about your faith through this service project

- a discussion of how you feel about choosing a vocation of service for yourself

For Extra Credit

While you are working on your project, read one or more of these books for inspiration. Include a written summary of the book with your report.

Dear, John, S.J. *Mary of Nazareth: Prophet of Peace*. Notre Dame, Ind.: Ave Maria Press, 2003.

Elgin, Duane. *Voluntary Simplicity: Toward a Way of Life That Is Outwardly Simple, Inwardly Rich*. New York: Morrow, 1993.

Giono, Jean. *The Man Who Planted Trees*. Chelsea, Vt.: Chelsea Green Publishing Co., 1985.

Hanson, Stephanie Weller. *Mountains of the Moon: Stories about Social Justice*. Winona, Minn.: St. Mary's Press, 1998.

Ingram, Catherine. *In the Footsteps of Gandhi: Conversations with Spiritual Social Activists*. Berkeley, Calif.: Parallax Press, 1990.

King, Martin Luther, Jr. *The Trumpet of Conscience*. New York: Harper & Row, 1968.

Kozel, Jonathan. *Rachel and Her Children: Homeless Families in America*. New York: Crown Publishers, 1988.

Larned, Marianne, ed. *Stone Soup for the World: Life-Changing Stories of Kindness & Courageous Acts of Service*. York Beach, Maine: Conari Press, 1998.

Schumacher, E. F. *Small Is Beautiful: Economics as if People Mattered*. New York: Harper & Row, 1973.

Seo, Danny. *Generation React: Activism for Beginners*. New York: Ballantine, 1997.

Statements of Catholic policy on social justice and social policy, plus more suggestions for service projects and justice advocacy, can be found at the following Web site: http://www.usccb.org

Models of Spirituality

Have you ever heard the expression "All roads lead to China"? The phrase is used to express the idea that a variety of methods can be used to achieve a desired goal. The same is true for the Christian life. A variety of prayer styles, spiritual disciplines, and philosophical attitudes can be used to help us grow closer to Christ.

The phrase "Variety is the spice of life" also applies here. A rich variety of approaches to Christ helps prevent boredom and stagnation in our faith. The beautiful realization that God is totally beyond limits enables us to broaden our spiritual basis in order to grow from the wealth of experience of many others who have also sought to grow closer to Christ.

Male and Female

Part A.

Directions: The account in the Bible speaks of how humanity was created in the image and likeness of God—and thus humanity was created male and female. Because Jesus addressed God as "Abba" (literally "daddy"), we tend to think of God in masculine terms. Yet in the Hebrew language, there were no gender-specific pronouns used in reference to God. The books of Proverbs and Wisdom in the Old Testament personify and address God's Wisdom as a woman; today we interpret these references to Wisdom as God's feminine dimension. Other Scriptures refer to God as exhibiting feminine characteristics. Read the following passages, and summarize the image of God revealed in each. Determine whether the image is primarily masculine or feminine.

1. *Psalm 9:8–11*

2. *Isaiah 5:1–7*

3. *Isaiah 49:15*

4. *Isaiah 66:13*

5. *Hosea 11:1–4*

The vision of humanity as one enormous family, one objective tribe may once have been utopian. Now it is a practical necessity.

—Oscar Ichazo

139

Part B.

Directions: Answer the following questions.

1. Who has been a role model for you of what it means to be a man? a woman? What are some of the characteristics these people possess that would account for this? Describe how these people are models for you.

2. What types of messages did you get while growing up about what it means to be masculine? feminine?

3. What messages did you get about how men should express their emotions? about how women should express their emotions?

4. Describe a time in your growing-up experience when you had to suppress your emotions.

5. How do you react when a boy or man gets emotional?

6. How do you react when a girl or woman gets emotional?

The Journey toward the Masculine

Directions: Read the following information. Then complete items 1 and 2 as directed.

Masculine spirituality focuses on becoming like God, in whose image we have been created. Thus in each of us, there is both a masculine and a feminine dimension. The whole man, who is a holy man, is in touch with and comfortable with each of the dimensions within himself. He avoids society's false images of what it means to be masculine. Media often depict men who are macho, self-made and self-reliant, tough, resourceful, solely rational, denying feelings, exploiting others, aggressive, and insensitive.

In the book *The Wild Man's Journey*, Richard Rohr and Joseph Martos speak of a two-phase journey that becomes necessary for men seeking to develop a deeper spirituality. The first stage involves a journey toward discovering and accepting the feminine dimension in oneself. The second is a movement into a deeper masculine understanding, which involves getting in touch with the wild man within. The wild man is not a savage but is a natural man who has access to his full range of feelings and allows these feelings to temper his masculine energy by integrating it with the feminine. This energy is directed toward the external world that is a world of challenge and uncertainty.

Two men in the New Testament help to illustrate each of these aspects of the journey. The one described in John's Gospel is "the beloved disciple" is a model of one who has discovered the feminine dimension within himself. John the Baptist, to whose baptism and mentoring Jesus submitted, is a biblical model of the wild man. Both of these aspects must be integrated to become a full, spiritual man.

1. Read the following passages. Then write a brief character profile of each of these models, including the characteristics of masculinity which each reveals.

   a. The Beloved Disciple: *John 13:21–26*; *John 19:26–27*; *John 20:1–10*

All boys start out to be men. Some of them make it.

—Reverend Joseph L. Baglio

141

b.   John the Baptist: *Luke 3:1–20; Mark 6:17–29; John 1:19–34*

2.   In many tribal societies, at puberty boys undergo an initiation ritual
in order to be admitted into the men's world and enjoy the privi-
leges and responsibilities of their society as men. Often they
undergo a period of instruction and testing before they meet some
challenge as part of this initiation. Write about some of the ways
God calls us to a similar experience in our faith development.

The Woman's Creed

Directions: Read and reflect on the following profession of faith from a woman's perspective.

Upon pondering The Apostles' Creed and wondering what it would have been like had women wrote it . . .

I believe in God
who created woman and man in God's own image
who created the world
and gave both sexes
dominion over the earth.

I believe in Jesus
child of God
chosen of God
born of the woman Mary
who listened to women and liked them
who stayed in their homes
who discussed the Kingdom with them
who was followed and financed
by women disciples.

I believe in Jesus
who discussed theology with a woman at a well
and confided first in her
his messiahship
who motivated her to go and tell
her great news to the city.

I believe in Jesus who received anointing
from a woman at Simon's house
who rebuked the men guests who scorned her.
I believe in Jesus
who said this woman will be remembered
for what she did—
minister to Jesus.

I believe in Jesus
who acted boldly
to reject the blood taboo
of ancient societies
by healing the audacious woman
who touched him.

I believe in Jesus who healed
a woman on the Sabbath
and made her straight

Women, on the whole, bring special qualities of humanism, compassion, and creativity to society.

—Bella Abzug

143

because she was
a human being.

I believe in Jesus
who spoke of God
as a woman seeking the lost coin
as a woman who swept
seeking the lost.

I believe in Jesus
who thought of pregnancy and birth
with reverence
not as punishment—but
as a wrenching event
a metaphor for transformation
born again
anguish-into-joy.

I believe in Jesus
who spoke of himself
as a mother hen
who would gather her chicks
under her wings.

I believe in Jesus who appeared
first to Mary Magdalene
who sent her with the bursting message
GO AND TELL . . .

I believe in the wholeness
of the Savior
in whom there is neither
Jew nor Greek
slave nor free
male nor female
for we are all one
in salvation.

I believe in the Holy Spirit*
as she moves over the waters
of creation
and over the earth.

*The Hebrew word for *Spirit* is feminine.

Models of Spirituality

I believe in the Holy Spirit
as she yearns within us to
pray for those things
too deep for words.

I believe in the Holy Spirit
the woman spirit of God
who like a hen
created us
and gave us birth
and covers us
with her wings.[1]

[1]Rachel Conrad Wahlberg, "The Woman's Creed," in *Jesus and the Freed Woman*
(New York: Paulist Press, 1978), 155–57.

Action and Contemplation

Part A.

Directions: Action and contemplation are two dimensions of being human. While we may have more of one than the other, we need a balance of both. Jesus exemplified both in his life. He actively proclaimed God's reign in word and deed, and he frequently retired to pray and contemplate God his Father.

Place a checkmark on each continuum below to place yourself on the scale between the two contrasting characteristics. There is no correct answer. Choose the answer that describes you best.

When I think of myself, I feel I am

seeking variety .... seeking regularity

restless .... patient

a doer .... a thinker

a risk taker .... a security seeker

sociable .... preferring solitude

noisy .... quiet

a good talker .... a good listener

active .... passive

a server .... a prayer

> *I believe the important thing is not how we live but what we do in the day allotted us.*
>
> —Dr. Tom Dooley

146

Part B.

Directions: Read *Luke 10:38–41*, and answer the following questions.

1. With which character do you find it easier to identify—Mary or Martha? Explain your answer.

2. What possible meaning can we find in this scriptural passage?

3. Restate in your own words what St. Augustine is trying to convey when he says, "No man must be so committed to contemplation as, in his contemplation, to give no thought to his neighbor's needs, nor so absorbed in action as to dispense with the contemplation of God" (*City of God,* XIX, 19).

147

4. What light does this quotation shed on the story of Martha and Mary?

5. What does it mean to put our lives where our prayers are?

A Prayer of St. Ignatius of Loyola

Directions: Read the prayer of St. Ignatius, and reflect on the questions that follow.

> Take, Lord, and receive
> all my liberty, my memory,
> my understanding, and my entire will,
> all that I have and possess.
> You have given all to me.
> To you, Lord, I return it.
> All is yours.
> Dispose of it wholly according to your will.
> Give me your love and your grace,
> for this is enough for me.

1. How willing are you to offer your entire self to God as is stated in this prayer? Why do you think this is so?

2. Is God's love and grace sufficient for all of your needs and desires at this point in your life?

3. What areas of Ignatian spirituality could help you to grow in Christian maturity?

A Prayer of St. Francis of Assisi

Directions: Read the Prayer of St. Francis of Assisi, and use the questions to reflect on it.

> Lord, make me an instrument of your peace.
> Where there is hatred, let me sow love;
> where there is injury, pardon;
> where there is doubt, faith;
> where there is despair, hope;
> where there is darkness, light;
> where there is sadness, joy.
> O Divine Master, grant that I may not so much seek
> to be consoled as to console;
> to be understood as to understand;
> to be loved as to love.
> For it is in giving that we receive;
> it is in pardoning that we are pardoned;
> and it is in dying that we are born to eternal life.

1. How willing are you to become an instrument of God's peace as is outlined in this prayer? Why do you think this is so?

2. An old proverb states that it is more blessed to give than to receive. What are some of the benefits of giving?

3. What areas of Franciscan spirituality could help you to grow in Christian maturity?

Prayer for Serenity

Directions: Read the Prayer for Serenity, and use the questions to reflect on it.

> God, grant me
> serenity to accept the things I cannot change,
> courage to change the things I can and
> wisdom to know the difference—
> living one day at a time,
> enjoying one moment at a time—
> accepting hardship as a pathway to peace—
> taking, as Jesus did, this sinful world as it is,
> not as I would have it—
> trusting that you will make all things right
> if I surrender to your will—
> so that I may be reasonably happy in this life
> and supremely happy with you forever in the next.
> Amen.
>
> —Reinhold Niebuhr

1. What is serenity?

2. What are the ways I find serenity in my life?

3. What are some areas in my life that I cannot change but that rob me of serenity?

4. What areas of my life can I change to help me experience greater serenity?

5. What can I do to live one day at a time?

6. What are some of the areas in which I find it difficult to trust in God?

7. What are some of the obstacles that keep me from surrendering my will to God's will?

The Twelve Steps

Part A.

Directions: Read the Twelve Steps originated by Alcoholics Anonymous to help people change their lives. The steps are another example of a model for spirituality. As you read each step, think about how its contents show progress in the development of a spiritual life.

1. We admitted we were powerless over alcohol—that our lives had become unmanageable.

2. We came to believe that a Power greater than ourselves could restore us to sanity.

3. We made a decision to turn our will and our lives over to the care of God *as we understood Him.*

4. We made a searching and fearless moral inventory of ourselves.

5. We admitted to God, to ourselves, and to another human being the exact nature of our wrongs.

6. We were entirely ready to have God remove all these defects of character.

7. We humbly asked Him to remove our shortcomings.

8. We made a list of all persons we had harmed, and became willing to make amends to them all.

9. We made direct amends to such people wherever possible, except when to do so would injure them or others.

10. We continued to take personal inventory and when we were wrong, promptly admitted it.

11. We sought through prayer and meditation to improve our conscious contact with God, *as we understood Him*, praying for knowledge of His will for us and the power to carry that out.

12. Having had a spiritual awakening as the result of these steps, we tried to carry this message to alcoholics, and to practice these principles in all our affairs.[*]

[*]The Twelve Steps are reprinted with permission of Alcoholics Anonymous World Services, Inc. Permission to reprint and adapt does not mean that A.A. has reviewed or approved the contents of this publication nor that A.A. agrees with the views expressed herein. A.A. is a program of recovery from alcoholism—use of the Twelve Steps in connection with programs and activities which are patterned after A.A., but which address other problems, does not imply otherwise.

Part B.

Directions: Use the following questions to see how the Twelve Steps can relate to your own spiritual growth.

Step 1.   What are areas of my life where I experience powerlessness? where I experience unmanageability?

Step 2.   What are areas of insanity in my life where I do things that are not good for me? Do I believe God has the power to change my life?

Step 3.   What led me to turn my will and life over to the care of God? What has prevented me from doing so?

Step 4.   What do I believe are my greatest strengths? What do I see as my greatest weaknesses? How do I feel about taking an honest look at myself?

Step 5.   How comfortable do I feel admitting my wrongdoing to God? to another person? to myself?

Step 6.   What do I consider to be the greatest character defects that need to be addressed in my life?

Step 7.   Have I sought the Lord's help in changing my shortcomings? Have I come to recognize that there are areas I cannot change on my own?

Step 8.   Who are the three most important people in my life when I have harmed and with whom I must be reconciled?

Step 9.   What steps can I take to bring about a reconciliation with these people?

Step 10. How difficult is it for me to admit when I am wrong? Do I take time at the end of each day to take an honest look at myself and to see areas where I continue to need to change?

Step 11. What sort of daily prayer life do I have? Do I consciously seek God and try to grow in a deeper relationship with him? How important is it for me to know God's will? How do I come to know God's will for me?

Step 12. Have I ever had a spiritual awakening? In what ways do I share what God has shown me to help others who are dealing with similar problems?

152

"Hope Amidst Despair"—Ground Zero, September 11, 2001
Anne M. Bybee

Part 9

Stumbling Blocks

Like life, our faith in God has both ups and downs. At times, we are confronted with people, situations, and attitudes that may prove to be obstacles in our growth of faith. Sometimes these obstacles seem so big that our faith life may indeed suffer for a while. Other times, however, with the right choices, we can overcome the difficulties and enjoy a strengthened and renewed faith in Christ as a result.

The Book of Job: A Study Guide

Directions: The Book of Job addresses the timeless question: Why do bad things happen to good people? Suffering is a great stumbling block to faith in God. Why does God allow the innocent to suffer? Job represents all of us in his struggle to accept and understand the calamities that have befallen him. Read the assigned passages from the Book of Job, and answer the questions.

1. Read the Prologue to the Book of Job (*1:1–2:13*).

   a. What kind of a man was Job?

   b. Summarize the contest set up between Job and Satan.

   c. What was Job's first trial?

   d. How did Job react to this trial?

   e. What was Job's second trial?

   f. How did Job react to this second trial?

An optimist laughs to forget; a pessimist forgets to laugh.

2. Read parts of Eliphaz's, Bildad's, and Zophar's speeches, as well as Job's responses.

a. What reason did Eliphaz give for Job's misfortune (*4:1–8*)?

b. What advice did Eliphaz offer Job to end his trouble (*5:8–27*)?

c. What was Job's reply to Eliphaz (*6:24–29*)?

d. What reason did Bildad offer for Job's trouble (*8:1–10*)?

e. How did Job reply to Bildad (*9:1–15*)?

f. What advice did Zophar offer Job (*11:13–16*)?

g. What did Job say to his three friends after their speeches (chapter 13)?

3. Two more cycles of speeches follow in the Book of Job. Each cycle consists of the three friends trying to tell Job where he went wrong and Job defending his innocence. Then a young man named Elihu entered the debate and rehashed the same arguments. Job appealed to God directly for an answer about his suffering.

God did not answer any of Job's questions but rather let Job know that the answers are not simple. God's power and omniscience will never be understood by human beings. Job accepted this response and was comforted by God's presence to him in the midst of his suffering.

    a. What characterized the questions God began to fire at Job? (*38:1–18*)

    b. How did Job respond to God's questioning? (*40:1–6*)

    c. Why was God angry with Eliphaz? (*42:7–9*)

    d. What happened to Job after he prayed for Eliphaz? (*42:10–17*)

4. What is the main lesson of the Book of Job?

Two Sides of the Same Coin

Directions: We live in a world filled with contrasts: light and dark; summer and winter; warm and cold; life and death; good and bad; joy and sorrow. We often need these contrasts to put the realities of our lives into perspective. We appreciate family and friends more after a long absence from their presence, and we enjoy wearing shorts on the first warm day of spring after a long winter. Such appreciation and enjoyment are benefits for us. Suffering can produce benefits too. Examine the following list of painful or difficult experiences. Determine a benefit for each circumstance listed.

1. a woman laboring in childbirth

2. an athlete training two hours a day

3. a law student spending months preparing for the bar exam

4. a father of six holding down two jobs

5. having an abscessed tooth extracted

6. having the vet euthanize a sick family pet

7. losing a championship game

8. ending a relationship with someone you care about

9. moving away from your family home

10. standing up for your own beliefs even when you are the only one who thinks that way

Is the glass half-full or half-empty?

A Scriptural Path through Suffering

Directions: Use this exercise for private prayer.

So you feel as if your whole world has collapsed around you? Don't despair. Jesus felt that way too. (Read *Matthew 27:46*.) Sometimes just knowing that you are not alone can make all the difference in the world. Even in the midst of his suffering, Jesus trusted in God. (Read *Luke 23:46*.) We are called to do exactly the same.

Take a minute to place yourself in the loving presence of God. Share with God all your feelings. Remember Job? Remember the psalmists? Remember Jeremiah? None of them were afraid to yell at God or to tell God that they were hurt and angry. That's just the point— they told God how they really felt instead of turning away. Ask God to be present to you in the midst of your suffering.

Sooner or later each one of us struggles with loss. Sometimes the losses are small, but sometimes they are big. The biggest loss of all seems to be the death of a loved one. But God's love is so powerful that it will enable us to withstand whatever hardships life throws at us. (Read *Romans 8:35–39*.) Jesus faced a terrible trial. Through it all, he remained faithful to God. His resurrection shows all of us that nothing—not even death—can overcome the power of God's love. (Read *Romans 8:31–33*.)

When you are in the midst of suffering, remember the power that love can have in human life. People come into being as the result of the love between their parents. The force of love protects relationships from falling apart, protects children from harm, and enables miracles to happen. If our love, imperfect as it is, can accomplish so much, how much more can God's love protect us from harm and enable us to grow!

That's the real secret. We need to look at suffering as an opportunity to grow. (Read *Romans 5:3–5* and *James 1:2–4, 12*.) Remember, most of the time it is an exercise in frustration to seek the answer as to why suffering exists. The fact is, suffering exists. It happens to both good and bad people. Many times innocent people suffer and guilty people do not. It is just a fact of life. But God is love. God can work in all circumstances to bring hope when we are feeling the most hopeless, to bring strength when we feel the weakest, to bring peace when we are feeling the most anxious. All we have to do is ask, for nothing is impossible for God.

Earth has no sorrow that heaven cannot heal.

—Thomas More

159

Cult Cautions

Directions: Read the following information about cults and cult membership.

Definition

Cult is a label that has been applied to many religious and pseudoreligious groups. As a label, it is a term that is hard to define. Sometimes a group is called a cult because it is different or unusual. Sometimes a group is called a cult because it is feared or detested.

The appropriate use of the term *cult* is for a group that operates like a religion and is potentially dangerous or destructive to its members and others. Some religious groups possess one or the other of the following characteristics of potential danger. A few, the cults, possess many or all of them.

Characteristics of Potential Danger

1. There is a strong, charismatic, male leader who claims to be divine, to be a messiah, or to have received special spiritual revelations. There is often a double standard within the cult. The leader may be exempt from many of the requirements placed on his followers. He may live in luxury, while members live in an exceedingly simple lifestyle.

2. A rigid authority structure demands absolute loyalty from members.

3. Isolation from family, friends, and others outside the cult is required. Cults avoid investigation by outsiders and discourage criticism from within. They are paranoid about society, especially the government.

4. Followers are urged to turn their finances and other resources over to the group. Frequently, they are involved in fundraising activities for the group, or they work in businesses owned by the cult.

5. Doomsday messages on the imminent end of the world and the group's role in bringing about the end are taught. In preparation, the group possesses armed weapons.

Recruitment Techniques

1. Cults generally look for people who are in a period of transition— coming out of a broken relationship, in unfamiliar surroundings like college, dissatisfied with their traditional religious experience, or in similar circumstances which leave them vulnerable.

2. Cults tend to use deceptive practices such as identifying themselves as charitable organizations or youth groups that offer answers to complicated life situations.

3. They are often vague about their beliefs, insisting that these will be revealed once a person has undergone proper instruction.

4. They may make initial contact through giving away books or inviting people to lectures, retreats, parties, or dinners sponsored by the group.

5. They often invite people to their center to learn more about the group. Cults often use high-pressure brainwashing techniques, such as long, repetitive lectures and meals which are low in protein and high in sugar and starch. People are rarely without an accompanying cult member, and the schedule allows very little sleep. These practices dull a person's critical capacity and make him or her more receptive to indoctrination.

6. When people question, they are accused of either lacking faith or being deceived by evil forces.

Advice for You

1. Use common sense. Most people believe they are not susceptible to cult recruitment. They underestimate how subtle and persuasive cult recruiters can be.

2. Be cautious of any groups who show too much interest in your finances or background or who promise easy answers to life's problems.

3. Talk to other people about new experiences. Be open to their cautions and concerns.

161

4. Walk away when you feel pressured or rushed by people who want to tell you more about the organization with which they are involved.

The New Age Movement

Directions: Read the paragraph. Then use the chart to distinguish key beliefs of Christianity from teachings of the New Age Movement.

The New Age Movement has grown in popularity during recent years. It is a spiritual movement whose beliefs have been influenced by Eastern religions. It holds no formal doctrines, maintains that individuals are authorities unto themselves, has no membership requirements, and promotes no moral absolutes. As Adam and Eve in the temptation in the Garden were told by the serpent that they could be gods, the New Age Movement believes we are all gods and need no authority outside of ourselves. Many Christians have found New Age teaching appealing without recognizing that its precepts are incompatible with Christian belief and practice.

Topic	New Age Perspective	Christian Perspective
God	God is impersonal, a consciousness in all nature, the sum total of all that exists. Because everything is God, we are all gods. The New Age belief in God is basically pantheistic.	God is personal and loving. God has revealed himself to his creation in Jesus Christ. God is the creator distinct from creation. Humanity is created in the image and likeness of God, called to become like God, but we are not God.
Jesus	Jesus is an enlightened master, one of many such spiritual individuals who have discovered their own divinity. We can achieve the same level by discovering our higher self.	Jesus is God incarnate, fully human and fully divine. We acknowledge Jesus as Lord and Savior. Through his saving power, Jesus does for us what we are unable to do for ourselves.
Authority	Each individual must discover the authority within oneself through intuition and self-experience.	Christianity acknowledges Jesus Christ as Lord, Scripture as the revealed word of God, and the shared wisdom and experience of the Church. (See the *Catechism of the Catholic Church,* 1899.)
Human Dignity	Because each of us possesses unlimited potential, our dignity is seen in relation to how we have used our potential. Morality is something each of us determines for ourselves. Karma (fate) determines our destiny.	Our dignity is rooted in our being created in the image and likeness of God. God's gift of salvation affirms our worth, as we have received forgiveness and the call to God's kingdom through Jesus' death and resurrection.
The Supernatural	The New Age Movement sees this as a realm separate from the physical world. One enters this spiritual realm through an altered state of consciousness. This can occur through the use of such devices as Ouija boards, astrological charts, tarot cards or fortunetelling, or through channeling, a practice wherein one invites a spirit or entity to enter in and speak through him or her.	Christianity views this as surpassing the power of created beings; a result of God's gracious initiative. Our vocation to eternal life is supernatural. (See the *Catechism,* 1722 and 1998.)

Stumbling Blocks

Topic	New Age Perspective	Christian Perspective
Truth	The New Age Movement maintains that there is no absolute truth. All truth is relative to one's self-experience.	Christianity believes in God as absolute truth, in Jesus as the revelation of God, and in the necessity of always searching for whatever is true, wherever truth can be found—whether in the sciences or in religious faith. What is not true is not from God. Because lies, deceit, and error are always possible, the struggle for truth is essential to human life in its fullness. (See the *Catechism,* 215–16; see *John 8:32* and *John 14:6.*)
Salvation	Salvation consists of achieving one's divine self by realizing one's potential. There is no sin or guilt, only one's failure to discover one's true self.	Salvation is a gift of God, freely given, not earned. One enters into God's plan of salvation by establishing a relationship with Jesus, who won our salvation through his death. He promises us forgiveness for sins through repentance (See the *Catechism,* 169.)
Afterlife	One reaches enlightenment by seeking to fulfill one's destiny. This is accomplished through a series of lifetimes during repeated incarnations. We are then released from the cycle of reincarnations and lose our individual identity by becoming one with the cosmic "all."	We receive eternal life through Christ's death and resurrection. Our individuality is retained as we either share in God's kingdom or choose to reject that kingdom. (See the *Catechism,* 367 and 1721–22.)

163

Spiritual Deception

Directions: Read the following information. Then answer the questions.

The practice of satanism poses a serious danger to our spiritual health and well-being. There are three types of satanists. The first are those who belong to an organized, constitutionally-protected, satanic religion. Their principles do not espouse overt acts of violence or evil but rather promote self-centeredness and selfish pursuits. The second are those who belong to small, satanic cults. Frequently fueled by alcohol and drugs, they practice illegal, violent acts like grave desecration, animal sacrifice, ritual torture, and murder. The third type are those who dabble in satanic worship combined other occult practices, such as the use of crystals, fortunetelling, tarot cards, psychic healing, witchcraft, astrology, Ouija boards, channeling, and séances.

Whereas satanism deals with direct worship of Satan himself or of evil, occult involvement is not always seen as demonic. Yet all occult practices are forms of idolatry, as they seek guidance for one's life or power from something other than God. God sent the Holy Spirit to empower us with all that we need to live a spiritual life. He told us that we were to seek the spiritual realm only through him. Yet the occult promises guidance for our lives through other sources, something the Bible clearly prohibits.

In the Christian tradition, we use spiritual things to help us experience God and blessings for our lives. We call these things sacramentals. Holy water, blessed oil, and crucifixes are examples of sacramentals. Yet these things have no power in and of themselves. Their power stems from their source, a personal and loving God who uses them to draw us into a deeper union with him. In the occult world, though, material objects are seen as having power to heal or enlighten in themselves.

1. C. S. Lewis, the spiritual author, once wrote that the devil takes delight when people don't believe in his existence. Do you agree? Why or why not?

2. What advantage would the devil gain by excessive interest in him?

> *One of the best ways to safeguard yourself from being deceived is always to form the habit of looking at things for yourself, listening to things for yourself, thinking for yourself.*
>
> —Malcolm X

A Guide for Moral Decision Making

Directions: When you experience a moral dilemma (i.e., when you feel pulled in two directions at once and are uncertain of the right course to take), try to use the following guide to make your decision easier.

1. **Examine your motives**. Ask yourself these questions: What is really the issue here? Why do I want to do this? Will anybody be hurt by my decision? Is this a loving act? Will I be able to live with myself after I have made the decision? Motives based on selfishness, escaping personal responsibility for actions, and impulsiveness are rarely good ones for action.

2. **Consult the Scriptures**. Okay, so you will not find specific teachings of Jesus on the subject of gun control, war, euthanasia, premarital sex, drugs, and a lot of other subjects. You will find solid, important, and immensely practical insights into personal integrity, love of neighbor, honesty, the worth of human life, and other values. If you pay attention to these teachings, you will be able to face any type of dilemma.

3. **Investigate what the Church teaches**. The pope and the bishops have applied Christ's teachings to a variety of current social situations, including war, economics, family, prejudice, and work situations. The Holy Spirit has guided the Church through almost two thousand years of living in faithfulness to the Gospel message. The Church's teachings on morality are the benefits of that lived experience and can help us to decide the most loving course of action.

4. **Talk the situation over with someone you trust**—your parents, a sibling, a trusted friend, a school counselor, a priest, a pastoral minister—someone who has your best interests at heart. You can benefit from others asking you questions to clarify your motives. They can point out alternatives and insights that you may not have considered. They can support you, especially when your decision is particularly difficult.

5. **Pray for guidance. Remain open to the Spirit of God working in your heart. Remember the Lord's Prayer**—*Thy* will be done. Sincerely seek the Lord's direction for you in this particular action. Look for a sense of interior peace in your answer. Inner conflict and turmoil are a sign that the issue is not yet resolved.

6. **Follow your conscience.** Ultimately, you alone must decide what to do. Make sure your conscience is formed. Make the best, most loving choice for all parties concerned, and act accordingly.

7. **Accept the consequences.** Sometimes our decisions are not the right ones. If the decision was wrong, try to correct it if you can. Make amends if anyone was hurt. Accept responsibility. Receive the Sacrament of Reconciliation.

Stumbling Blocks

> *There comes a moment when you decide that some things should not be; then you have to act to try to stop those things.*
>
> —Marjorie Melville

165

A Self Test

Directions: Read the scriptural verse. Use the questions to examine how formed your conscience is at this point in your life. Take the necessary steps to improve your own formation.

> Examine yourselves to see whether you are living in faith. Test yourselves. Do you not realize that Jesus Christ is in you?—unless, of course, you fail the test.
>
> —*2 Corinthians 13:5*

1. Realistically speaking, how often do you make choices based on the principle of love? Review one day, and evaluate the choices you made according to Lawrence Kohlberg's theory. Record the number of times you made choices at each level.

   _____ To avoid getting into trouble

   _____ To get a reward

   _____ Because everybody else was doing it

   _____ Because you were "supposed to do it"

   _____ Because you sincerely believed in the principle behind the action

   _____ Because ultimately it was the most loving thing to do, even though you had to make a sacrifice to uphold this belief

2. According to this tally, what seems to be the primary motivation for your behavior?

3. Go back to your tally, and examine when these decisions were made. How many decisions were made on the spot, without time to think through the consequences?

   _____ How many were made in times of crisis?

   _____ How many were made after going through a decision-making process similar to the one outlined in **Exercise 80**?

4. How many of the decisions would you change now that you have the benefit of hindsight?

5. Do you learn from your previous decisions? What do your decisions teach you?

6. Are you, as the passage from *2 Corinthians* asks, living in faith? Explain.

Stumbling Blocks

Part 10

Ongoing Formation

You are near graduation, and this is the last chapter of the book, but that does not mean that you are off the hook just yet. Mature Christians are never off the hook. Our spiritual life demands constant attention and nurturing. Once you are on your own, you will need to take personal responsibility for your own faith development.

This section is designed to give you some of the tools you need to live out the rest of your life as a spiritually mature adult Christian who wants to maintain a happy and healthy faith relationship with Jesus Christ. Good luck, and may God bless you on your journey towards the kingdom!

Steps for Growth

Part A.

Directions: All the baptized are called to be holy. One way of thinking about being holy is thinking about being fully alive. To be fully alive is to live in the fullest way possible, including our relationships with God and others. In his book *The Search for Significance*, Robert S. McGee identifies four false beliefs which prevent us from experiencing that fullness of life. Read each of the statements, and list possible consequences that could result from holding each of these false beliefs. Then reflect on how these beliefs may have become part of your perception of yourself.

1. I must meet certain standards in order to feel good about myself.

   Consequences

2. I must be approved (accepted) by others to feel good about myself.

   Consequences

3. Those who fail are unworthy of love and deserve to be punished.

   Consequences

4. I am what I am. I cannot change. I am hopeless.

   Consequences

   • Which of these false beliefs have I come to believe?

   • How has the acceptance of these false beliefs affected the way I live?

A full life and a great love: this is the incomparable privilege and dutiful goal of every Christian.

—Reverend William McNamara, O.C.D.

169

Part B.

Directions: In his book *Fully Human, Fully Alive*, John Powell, S.J., describes five steps necessary in order to experience the fullness of life. They are as follows:

- to accept myself
- to be myself
- to forget myself in loving
- to believe
- to belong

Which of these steps do you find the hardest? Why?

How could you make progress toward achieving this difficult step in your life?

Goals for Growth

Directions: Indicate briefly and realistically what you want to accomplish in the future in the following areas of your life. Consider short-term goals as those you could accomplish in one or two years. Long-term goals might require five to fifteen years.

Physical Well-Being

Short-term goals

Long-term goals

Spiritual Life

Short-term goals

Long-term goals

Home and Family Life

Short-term goals

Long-term goals

Financial Status

Short-term goals

Long-term goals

The future will be different if we make the present different.

—Peter Maurin

171

Emotional Health

    Short-term goals

    Long-term goals

Social Responsibility/Activities/Justice

    Short-term goals

    Long-term goals

Intellectual Development

    Short-term goals

    Long-term goals

What one thing could I change in my life at this time that would give me the greatest peace of mind? What steps could I take that would bring me to the point of making that change?

Living the Christian Life

Directions: Read and reflect on the following analogy.

Imagine an old-fashioned wheel of the sort used on covered wagons. At the center was the hub. The hub radiated the power through the spokes to the outer wheel, enabling the wheel to move. This wheel can serve as an analogy to living the Christian life.

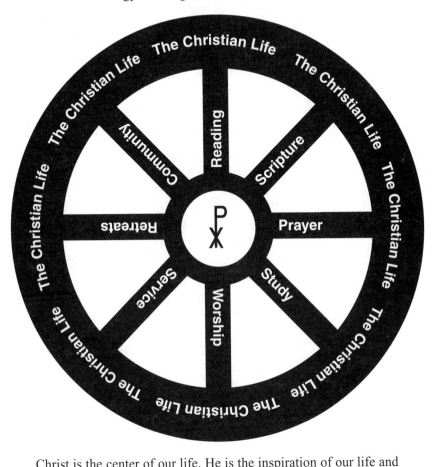

173

Christ is the center of our life. He is the inspiration of our life and the source of our power. We cannot live as Christians without being rooted in a relationship with him. He gives meaning to living a Christian lifestyle. We need to give ourselves the chance to grow in Christ. The way we relate with Christ in love enhances our life and the way we relate to others.

Christ, therefore, is the hub of our lives. As we grow in him, we receive the power to live transformed lives. The outer wheel, the Christian life, is our response to God's love. It witnesses to what we have experienced in our relationship with him, and it seeks to share what we have received with others. The spokes are the avenues by which we do this. As we practice these spiritual disciplines, we both better understand our Christian calling and more effectively live the Christian vocation.

Ongoing Formation

A Strategy for Spiritual Fitness

Directions: Use this exercise to generate a plan for your improved spiritual fitness.

Willingness without action is fantasy.

1. Explain what this sentence means to you.

Always begin somewhere. You can't build a reputation on what you intend to do.

174

2. How does this sentence apply to living a Christian life?

3. List eight practical things you can do to grow in your relationship with Jesus over the next five years, to grow in spiritual fitness. Try to choose something from each of the eight spokes of the Christian life wheel.

Some Things to Consider

Directions: In order to understand and profit from reading the spiritual classics, it is necessary to approach the material with some plan of action. Use the following steps as a guide to organized reading.

1. Determine the background for the text. Read the critical notes and biographical details in the prologue or introduction to the text to determine the author's framework.

    - When was this written?

    - What world and church events influenced the time this piece was written?

    - Who was the author? What do you know about him or her?

2. Determine the author's understanding of God.

    - How is God described in the text?

    - How is the author's understanding of God similar to what is in Scripture? How is it different?

    - Do you think the author's cultural context influenced his or her perception of God?

3. Determine the author's understanding of people.

    - How does the author see humanity relating to God?

    - Does the author portray humanity optimistically or pessimistically?

    - Does the author deal with the subject of sin? If so, how does the author understand sin?

    - Does the author deal with the subject of grace? If so, what does the author say about grace?

4. Determine the author's understanding of community.

    - Does the author talk about the community's or just the individual's relationship with God?

    - How does the author view the Church?

    - Does the author describe an individual's responsibility to the community?

5. Determine the author's spiritual approach.

    - Is this work intellectually centered?

    - Is this work emotionally centered?

    - Is this work symbolic in approach?

    - Is this work nonsymbolic in approach?

After three days without reading, talk becomes flavorless.

—Chinese Proverb

175

6. Determine your reaction to the text.

- How do you feel about the author's understanding of God, people, and community?

- Did you gain any insight into your own spiritual development from reading this text?

- Would you recommend this book to a friend? Why or why not?

Suggested Book List

Directions: Read one of the following books. Use **Exercise 86** as a guide for reflection.

Classics of Western Spirituality Series

Armstrong, Regis J., and Ignatius C. Brady, tr. *Francis and Clare: The Complete Works*. New York: Paulist Press, 1982.

Bond, Lawrence H., tr. *Nicholas of Cusa: Selected Spiritual Writings*. New York: Paulist Press, 1997.

Clark, Mary T., tr. *Augustine of Hippo: Selected Writings*. New York: Paulist Press, 1984.

Colledge, Edmund, et al., eds. *Julian of Norwich: Showings*. New York: Paulist Press, 1978.

Colledge, Edmund, and Bernard McGinn, tr. *Meister Eckhart: The Essential Sermons, Commentaries, Treatises, and Defense*. New York: Paulist Press, 1986.

Donelly, Patrick, and Ronald J. Teske, eds. *Robert Bellarmine: Spiritual Writings*. New York: Paulist Press, 1989.

Kavanaugh, Karen, and Otilio Rodrigues, tr. *Teresa of Avila: The Interior Castle*. New York: Paulist Press, 1979.

Ker, Ian, tr. *John Henry Newman: Selected Sermons*. New York: Paulist Press, 1994.

Noffke, Suzanne, ed. *Catherine of Siena: The Dialogue*. New York: Paulist Press, 1980.

Steere, Douglas V., ed. *Quaker Spirituality: Selected Writings*. New York: Paulist Press, 1984.

Whaling, Frank, ed. *John and Charles Wesley: Selected Writings and Hymns*. New York: Paulist Press, 1981.

Other Classical Works

à Kempis, Thomas. *The Imitation of Christ*. Translated by Ronald Knox and Michael Oakley. New York: Sheed & Ward, 1959.

Ignatius of Loyola. *Spiritual Exercises*. Translated by Louis J. Puhl. Westminster, Md.: Newman Press, 1951.

John of the Cross. *Dark Night of the Soul*. Translated by E. Allison Peers. Garden City, N.Y.: Image Books, 1959.

Lewis, C. S. *Mere Christianity*. New York: Macmillan, 1952.

———. *Surprised by Joy*. New York: Harcourt, Brace & World, 1955.

Merton, Thomas. *Conjectures of a Guilty Bystander*. New York: Doubleday, 1989.

———. *The Seven Storey Mountain*. San Diego: Harcourt Brace Jovanovich, 1990.

> *The man who does not read good books has no advantage over the man who can't read.*
>
> —Mark Twain

177

Pascal. *Pensees*. Translated by Martin Turnell. New York: Harper & Bros., 1962.

Teilhard de Chardin, Pierre. *The Divine Milieu*. New York: Harper, 1960.

———. *The Future of Man*. New York: Harper & Row, 1964.

Teresa of Avila. *The Way of Perfection*. Translated by E. Allison Peers. Garden City, N.Y.: Image Books, 1991.

Therese of Lisieux. *Story of a Soul*. Translated by Michael Day Trabuco. Canyon, Calif.: Source Books CA, 1991.

More Twentieth-Century Classics

Bonhoeffer, Diedrich. *The Cost of Discipleship*. Trans. R. H. Fuller. New York: Macmillan, 1959.

Day, Dorothy. *The Long Loneliness*. San Francisco: Harper, 1981.

Hammarskjold, Dag. *Markings*. Translated by Leif Sotberg and W. H. Auden. New York: Ballantine Books, 1983.

Nouwen, Henri J. M. *Making All Things New*. San Francisco: Harper, 1981.

———. *The Way of the Heart*. New York: Ballantine Books, 1985.

———. *Reaching Out*. New York: Doubleday, 1986.

Powell, John. *Fully Human, Fully Alive*. Allen, Tex.: Tabor Publishing, 1989.

Rahner, Karl. *The Practice of Faith: A Handbook of Contemporary Spirituality*. New York: Crossroads Publishing, 1986.

Schweitzer, Albert. *Out of My Life*. Translated by Antje Bultmann Lemke. New York: H. Holt, 1990.

Stein, Edith. *Essential Writings*. Ed. John Sullivan. Maryknoll, N.Y.: Orbis Books, 2002.

Underhill, Evelyn. *Concerning the Inner Life*. Chatham, N.Y.: One World Pubns., Ltd., 1992.

Weil, Simone. *Waiting for God*. Translated by Emma Cranfurd. New York: Harper & Row, 1973.

Easy Reading

Bloom, Anthony. *Beginning to Pray*. Mahwah, N.J.: Phoenix Press, 1970.

Capra, Fritjof. *Uncommon Wisdom*. New York: Simon & Schuster, 1988.

Cash, Johnny. *Man in White*. San Francisco: Harper SanFrancisco, 1986.

Crimp, Susan. *Touched by a Saint: Personal Encounter with Mother Teresa*. Notre Dame, Ind.: Ave Maria Press, 2000.

Doyle, Brian. *Saints Passionate and Peculiar*. Winona, Minn.: St. Mary Press, 2002.

Elie, Paul. *The Life You Save May Be Your Own.* New York: Farrar, Straus and Giroux, 2003.

Frankl, Viktor E. *Man's Search for Meaning.* Cutchogue, N.Y.: Buccaneer Books, 1992.

Gallagher, Michelle. *Reason Is Beguiled: On the Mystery of Martyrdom and the Total Self-Gift.* New York: Alba House, 2000.

Girzone, Joseph. *Joshua.* Albany, N.Y.: Richelieu Court, 1983.

———. *Joshua and the Children.* New York: Macmillan, 1989.

———. *Joshua in the Holy Land.* New York: Macmillan, 1989.

Greene, Graham. *Burnt-Out Case.* New York: Viking Press, 1961.

Gruber, Mark, O.S.B. *Journey Back to Eden: My Life and Times Among the Desert Fathers.* Maryknoll, N.Y.: Orbis, 2002.

Huebsch, Bill. *Praying with Pope John XXIII.* Winona, Minn.: St. Mary Press, 1999.

Kohn, Howard. *The Last Farmer.* New York: Summit Books, 1988.

Kun, Jeanne, editor. *Even Unto Death: Wisdom from Modern Martyrs.* Ijamsville, Md.: The Word Among Us Press, 2002.

McCarthy, Patricia. *Of Passion and Folly: A Scriptural Foundational for Peace.* Collegeville, Minn.: The Liturgical Press, 1998.

Miller, Walter M. *A Canticle for Leibowicz.* Philadelphia: Lippincott, 1959.

Monette, Paul. *Borrowed Time—An AIDS Memoir.* San Diego: Harcourt Brace Jovanovich, 1988.

Muggeridge, Malcolm. *Something Beautiful for God.* New York: Harper & Row, 1971.

Nolan, Mary Catherine, O.P. *Mary's Song: Living Her Timeless Prayer.* Notre Dame, Ind.: Ave Maria Press, 2001.

Oben, Freda Mary, tr. *Edith Stein: Essays on Woman.* 2d ed. Washington D.C.: ICS Publications, 1996.

Rolheiser, Ronald. *The Holy Longing: The Search for a Christian Spirituality.* New York: Doubleday, 1999.

Steinbeck, John. *To a God Unknown.* Leicester, England: Lilverscroft, 1974.

Ten Boom, Corrie. *The Hiding Place.* Washington Depot, Conn.: Chosen Books, 1971.

Thornton, Lawrence. *Imagining Argentina.* Garden City, N.Y.: Doubleday, 1987.

———. *Under the Gypsy Moon.* New York: Doubleday, 1990.

Vitek, John M. *My Dear Young Friends: Pope John Paul II Speaks to Teens on Life, Love and Courage.* Winona, Minn.: St. Mary Press, 2001.

Walters, Kerry. *Spirituality of the Handmaid: A Model for Contemporary Seekers.* New York: Paulist Press, 1999.

Dear Gabby

Directions: Consider the values we may pick up in our culture. On the one hand, we hear about how important it is to work and study hard, take the best classes, participate in the best sports and activities, work a part-time job to make money, spend as much time as we can being involved and productive. Sometimes it seems that we can get so caught up in work, study, sports, and the other busy activities of life that we feel as if we don't have time to breathe. On the other hand, we hear that life is about "having fun;" that in whatever we do, we should be having fun doing it. There seem to be lots of entertainment industries surrounding us, eager to take our money and deliver us to a fun time. Which is more important in life: work or play? In a healthy adult spirituality, how do we maintain a balance between the two? Read each of the following letters, and offer your advice to the writers.

Dear Gabby,

I am a high school senior, and I feel as though I can't cope anymore. I've got a full load of classes including calculus, physics, a fourth year of French, and Advanced Placement English. I'm working every day after school until 11 P.M. and on weekends to get some money together for college, and now my boyfriend is screaming at me because we don't spend any time together any more. Five college applications are sitting on my desk waiting to be filled out, and the deadline is next week. I haven't even started the required essay for each of them yet, and I don't even want to think about when I'll be able to study for the college entrance exams. Everything is important, and all of it has to get done. I just don't think I can do this anymore. *Help!*

Tired in Texas

Dear Tired,

Dear Gabby,

I am so bored! School's a drag. There's nothing good on television anymore. I'm tired of just hanging out at the mall. I used to live in New York, and there was plenty for my friends and me to do there. This town is dead. There's nothing for a guy to do around here. Any suggestions?

Really Yawning

Dear Yawning,

Dear Gabby,

I wish everybody would get off my back! Okay, so I'm not doing too hot in school right now, but who cares?! I just live for weekends because I always have a good time with my friends. We talk on the phone all the time and hang out together—there's just not enough time to get homework done. Besides, it's boring anyway. When am I actually going to use American history anyway? So what's the problem, you ask? My folks say I have to get a job this summer. I don't want to. They say it will teach me some responsibility. I don't think it will. Besides, I want to sleep in every day. I have to get up at 6 A.M. for school, and I'm tired. I really want to go camping with my friends for a couple of weeks. How can I convince my parents that this work thing is a bad idea?

Party Hardy

Dear Party,

And on the Seventh Day, God Rested

Directions: Use the following exercise to pull together your understanding of the importance of both work and leisure.

1. Summarize briefly each of the following scriptural passages. Comment on what each passage teaches us.

    a. *Genesis 2:1–4*

    b. *Exodus 20:8–11*

    c. *Deuteronomy 5:12–15*

    d. *Mark 2:23–28*

2. Read the quotations below and answer the questions.

    > All people have "the right to rest and leisure, including reasonable limitation of working hours and periodic holidays with pay," and "the right freely to participate in the cultural life of the community, to enjoy the arts and to share in scientific advancement and its benefits."
    >
    > —Universal Declaration of Human Rights

    > We hold these truths to be self evident, that all men are created equal, that they are endowed by their creator with certain unalienable rights, that among these are Life, Liberty, and the Pursuit of Happiness.
    >
    > —Declaration of Independence

    a. Why are rest, leisure, and the pursuit of happiness fundamental rights of human beings?

    b. What happens to us when our needs for rest and work are out of balance?

Giving attention to leisure can spell the difference between killing time and being free and relaxed enough to take in all that is good in life.

—Dennis G. Geaney, O.S.A.

182

Pray Always

Directions: Read the following scriptural passages to discover how we are to pray.

Matthew 5:44

John 14:13

Luke 11:1–4

Luke 18:1

Luke 21:36

Luke 11:5–13

Matthew 6:5–8

Romans 12:12

1 Timothy 4:4–5

1 John 14–15

1 Timothy 2:1–8

1 Thessalonians 5:16–18

Colossians 3:15–17

We obtain everything from God according to the measure of our confidence.

—St. Therese

Praying with the Church

Directions: As a class, pray together the following prayer modeled on the Church's Liturgy of the Hours.

Hymn: (Choose a familiar song.)

Psalm 27:1, 4, 7–8, 13–14

Reader 1: The Lord is my light and my help; whom shall I fear?

All: The Lord is my light and my help; whom shall I fear?

Reader 1: The LORD is my light and my salvation;
   whom do I fear?
   The LORD is my life's refuge;
   of whom am I afraid?

All: The Lord is my light and my help; whom shall I fear?

Reader 1: One thing I ask of the LORD;
   this I seek:
   To dwell in the LORD's house
   all the days of my life,
   To gaze on the LORD's beauty,
   to visit his temple.

All: The Lord is my light and my help; whom shall I fear?

Reader 2: I long to look on you, O Lord;
   do not turn your face from me.

All: I long to look on you, O Lord;
   do not turn your face from me.

Reader 2: Hear my voice LORD, when I call;
   have mercy on me and answer me.
   "Come," says my heart, "seek God's face";
   your face, LORD, do I seek!

All: I long to look on you, O Lord;
   do not turn your face from me.

Reader 2: I believe I shall enjoy the LORD's
   goodness
   in the land of the living.
   Wait for the LORD, take courage;
   be stouthearted, wait for the LORD.

All: I long to look on you, O Lord;
   do not turn your face from me.

Leader: Creator God, give us your strength to live in
   hope all our days. Keep us close to you in
   times of trial and difficulty.

184

Revelation 15:3

Reader 3: Glory to God forever!

All: Glory to God forever!

Reader 3: "Great and wonderful are your works,
        Lord God almighty.
    Just and true are your ways,
        O king of the nations.

All: Glory to God forever!

Reader 3: Who will not fear you, Lord,
    or glorify your name?

All: Glory to God forever!

Reader 3: For you alone are holy.
        All the nations will come
        and worship before you,
        for your righteous acts have been revealed."

All: Glory to God forever!

Ephesians 3:14–21

Reader 4: (Read the passage from Ephesians aloud.)

Quiet reflection

Canticle of Mary—*Luke 1:46–55*

All: "My soul proclaims the greatness of the Lord;
        my spirit rejoices in God my savior.
    For he has looked upon his handmaid's lowliness;
        behold, from now on will all ages call me blessed.
    The Mighty One has done great things for me,
        and holy is his name.
    His mercy is from age to age
        to those who fear him.
    He has shown might with his arm,
        dispersed the arrogant of mind and heart.
    He has thrown down the rulers from their thrones
        but lifted up the lowly.
    The hungry he has filled with good things;
        the rich he has sent away empty.
    He has helped Israel his servant,
        remembering his mercy,
    according to his promise to our fathers,
        to Abraham and to his descendants forever."

Leader: Let us lift our petitions to the Lord who answers our needs.

All: Lord, hear our prayer.

Leader: Inspire our governmental leaders to pursue peace with justice and dignity for all people.

All: Lord, hear our prayer.

Leader: May all people seek you with pure and sincere hearts.

All: Lord, hear our prayer.

Leader: Accept our prayers for our own intentions, mentioned now in silence . . .

All: Lord, hear our prayer.

All: (Recite the Lord's Prayer.)

Leader: Lord God,
watch over us.
Keep us close to you in all we do.
May our lives be a constant prayer to you.

All: Amen.

Closing Prayer Service

Directions: Use the following guide to make your own prayer service based upon the model of the Liturgy of the Hours.

1. Choose a song that everybody can sing. The hymn should offer praise or thanksgiving to God.

2. Pick a psalm to recite antiphonally, with a response between the verses. Consider, for example, *Psalms 24, 67, 95,* or *100.* With 150 psalms to choose from, you are sure to find one that fits the mood you are trying to create.

3. Choose a reading from Scripture. Your text is full of many different suggestions. Look back through the book, choose one or two passages that have special meaning for you, and incorporate them into the prayer service.

4. Allow some quiet time for meditation. Consider opening the time up for shared reflection on the readings.

5. Compose some petitions. Remember in prayer the universal Church (with the pope, bishops, priests, sisters, and laity), world governmental leaders, your own local needs, and the poor.

6. Remember to recite the Lord's Prayer together.

7. Add a few closing words, and you are ready to assign roles to the people in your class.

Acknowledgments

Introduction

For use of the poem "Faith" by Terry Anderson from *Den of Lions: Memoirs of Seven Years*, Crown Publishing Group, 1993. Used with permission of the author.

Parts 2, 5, and 7 Divider Pages

For use of artwork by Timothy P. Schmalz: "Father," "Christ Washing Peter's Feet," and "A Warm Embrace." Web: www.sculpturebytps.com; Phone: (800) 590-3264.

Parts 3 and 10 Divider Pages

For use of the photographs "Yellow Rose" and "Pioneer Trail" by Linda Valasik, H.M. Courtesy Linda Valasik, H.M. E-mail: lvalasik@ centerforlearning.org.

Exercise 23

For use of excerpts from *Man's Search for Meaning* by Viktor E. Frankl. Copyright © 1959, 1962, 1984, 1992 by Viktor E. Frankl. Reprinted by permission of Beacon Press, Boston.

Part 4 Divider Page

For use of STScI-PRC2003-32a. ESA, NASA, and Robert A. E. Fosbury (European Space Agency/Space Telescope-European Coordinating Facility, Germany).

Exercise 46

For use of excerpts adapted from *The Positive Power of Christ* by Norman Vincent Peale, © 1980. Used by permission of Tyndale House Publishers, Inc. All rights reserved.

Part 6 Divider Page

For use of "The Return" by Beverly Steigerwald. Courtesy of Creator Mundi, Inc. Web: www.creatormundi.com. The Gallery of Sacred Art, Denver, Colorado.

Exercise 57 Sidebar

For use of "Vespers" by A. A. Milne from *When We Were Very Young* by A. A. Milne, illustrations by E. H. Shepard, copyright 1924 by E. P. Dutton, renewed 1952 by A. A. Milne. Used by permission of Dutton Children's Books, A Division of Penguin Young Readers Group, A Member of Penguin Group (USA) Inc., 345 Hudson Street, New York, NY 10014. All rights reserved.

Exercise 68

For use of "The Woman's Creed" from *Jesus and the Freed Woman* by Rachel Conrad Wahlberg. Copyright 1978 by The Missionary Society of St. Paul the Apostle. Reprinted by permission of Paulist Press.

Faith: Developing an Adult Spirituality

Exercise 73

For use of the Twelve Steps. The Twelve Steps are reprinted with permission of Alcoholics Anonymous World Services, Inc. Permission to reprint and adapt the Twelve Steps does not mean that A.A. has reviewed or approved the contents of this publication nor that A.A. agrees with the views expressed herein. A.A. is a program of recovery from alcoholism—use of the Twelve Steps in connection with programs and activities which are patterned after A.A., but which address other problems, does not imply otherwise.

Part 9 Divider Page

For use of the photograph "Hope Amidst Despair" by Anne M. Bybee. Courtesy of Anne M. Bybee. E-mail: Anne.Bybee@emsa.ca.gov.

1

The Publisher

All instructional materials identified by the TAP® (Teachers/Authors/Publishers) trademark are developed by a national network of 400 teacher-authors, whose collective educational experience distinguishes the publishing objective of The Center for Learning, a nonprofit educational corporation founded in 1970.

Concentrating on values-related disciplines, the Center publishes humanities and religion curriculum units for use in public and private schools and other educational settings. Approximately 600 language arts, social studies, novel/drama, life issues, and faith publications are available.

While acutely aware of the challenges and uncertain solutions to growing educational problems, the Center is committed to quality curriculum development and to the expansion of learning opportunities for all students. Publications are regularly evaluated and updated to meet the changing and diverse needs of teachers and students. Teachers may offer suggestions for development of new publications or revisions of existing titles by contacting

The Center for Learning
Administration/Creative Development
P.O. Box 417, Evergreen Road
Villa Maria, PA 16155
(724) 964-1601 • FAX (724) 964-1802

The Center for Learning
Editorial/Prepress
24600 Detroit Road, Suite 201
Westlake, OH 44145
(440) 250-9341 • FAX (440) 250-9715

For a free catalog containing order and price information and a descriptive listing of titles, contact

The Center for Learning
Customer Service
P.O. Box 910, Evergreen Road
Villa Maria, PA 16155
(724) 964-8083 • (800) 767-9090
FAX (888) 767-8080
http://www.centerforlearning.org